Carnivorous Plants

Carnivorous

Alphabooks

A & C Black · London

Plants

Adrian Slack

Photographs by Jane Gate

CARNIVOROUS PLANTS

This revised edition published by Alphabooks Ltd
Sherborne, Dorset DT9 3LU
A subsidiary of A & C Black Plc
35 Bedford Row, London WC1R 4JH

First published in Great Britain in 1979.

ISBN: 0 7136 3079 5

All line drawings are by the author

British Library Cataloguing in Publication Data

Slack, Adrian
Carnivorous plants.—Rev. ed.
1. Carnivorous plants
I. Title
581

ISBN 0-7136-3079-5

Printed by BAS Printers Limited, Over Wallop, Hampshire, England

Contents

Acknowledgments *page* 6
List of Colour Plates 7
Preface 8

Description

1 The Carnivorous Plants: An Introduction 11
2 The Pitcher Plants of Continental America 21
The Sun Pitchers: *Heliamphora* 21
The Trumpet Pitchers: *Sarracenia* 25
The Cobra Lily: *Darlingtonia* 71
3 The Tropical Pitcher Plant: *Nepenthes* 75
4 The West Australian Pitcher Plant: *Cephalotus* 89
5 *Genlisea* 92
6 The Passive Flypapers 95
The Rainbow Plant: *Byblis* 95
The Portuguese Sundew: *Drosophyllum* 99
7 The Active Flypapers 103
The Butterworts: *Pinguicula* 104
The Sundews: *Drosera* 119
8 The Spring Traps 155
The Venus Fly Trap: *Dionaea* 155
The Waterwheel Plant: *Aldrovanda* 161
9 The Bladder Traps 165
The Bladderworts: *Utricularia* 165
The Pink Petticoats: *Polypompholyx* 180

Cultivation

10 How to grow Carnivorous Plants 183
Cultivation indoors 183
Greenhouse cultivation 186
Cultivation out of doors 190
Containers and materials 193
Species cultivation 196
Appendix 1 Raising *Sarracenia* hybrids 228
Appendix 2 *Triphyophyllum* 231
Appendix 3 *Nepenthes* horticultural hybrids 233
Bibliography and References 234
List of Suppliers 235
Glossary 236
Index 238

Acknowledgments

In the preparation of this book my path was made the easier by much valuable information and assistance freely given to me by others. From that leading authority on the cultivation of carnivorous plants, Mr Joseph Mazrimas of California, I received much helpful advice, and I am entirely indebted to him for all information on the cultivation of *Heliamphora* on which he is the acknowledged expert. I am also grateful to the two commercial growers, Mr Timothy Heneage of Marston Exotics, and Mr Robert Hanrahan of World Insectivorous Plants for their kindness in placing their considerable experience at my disposal. In her photographs Jane Gate not only shows a convincing portrait of each subject, but seldom fails to convey an indefinable 'feeling' evoked by it. She has at last persuaded me that photography in her hands if in no other is an art, and I thank her for her unending patience.

Amongst others to whom I am grateful are Professor T. Lawrence Mellichamp of the University of North Carolina at Charlotte, Mr Jay Brodie, Mr Joseph P. Contasano, Mr Patrick Dwyer, Mr James Fife, Mr Paul J. Lewis, Mr Robert Louis Muller, Mr Phillip Sheridan, and Mr Warren Stoutamire, all of the United States, to Mr Jim Korolas of Canada, to Mr Phillip Mann of Western Australia, and in Great Britain to Mr Terry Brokenbro, Mr David Taylor, and by no means least to Mr John Watkins who has the distinction of being the founder and chief architect of the thriving Carnivorous Plant Society.

I was given much assistance by officials and staff of the Royal Botanic Gardens, Kew, the University Botanic Garden at Oxford, the libraries of the British Museum (Natural History) and by Mr Michael Cole and Mr Norman Parker of the Biology Dept, Millfield School. Their hordes of attendant pupil-botanists remain as yet uneaten by some impressive *Dionaea, Drosera, Sarracenia* and one vast boa constrictor.

There are many others who have provided assistance indirectly, and I would mention Mr G. A. Sergeant for much help in the early days of my collection, and that great experimenter in the cultivation and propogation of carnivorous plants, Mr Stephen Clemesha of New South Wales. Lastly, I extend my thanks to Leslie and Anthony Birks-Hay for their work in producing the book, and for their remarkable patience in awaiting the text.

List of Colour Plates

	page
Trumpet Pitchers *Sarracenia flava* and *Sarracenia* x *catesbaei*	33
Trumpet Pitcher *Sarracenia leucophylla*	34
Trumpet Pitcher *Sarracenia alata* 'Redthroat'	51
Trumpet Pitcher hybrid *Sarracenia* x *mitchelliana*	52
Trumpet Pitcher hybrid *Sarracenia* x *excellens*	69
The Cobra Lily *Darlingtonia californica*	70
Tropical Pitcher Plant hybrid *Nepenthes* x *williamsii*	87
West Australian Pitcher Plant *Cephalotus follicularis*	88
Butterwort *Pinguicula grandiflora*	105
Butterworts *Pinguicula caudata* and *Pinguicula mexicana*	106
Fork-leaved Sundew *Drosera binata dichotoma*	123
South African Sundew *Drosera aliciae*	124
Venus Fly Trap *Dionaea muscipula*	157
Pygmy Sundew *Drosera dichrosepala*	158
Trumpet Pitcher hybrid *Sarracenia* 'Marston Mill'	175
Trumpet Pitcher hybrid *Sarracenia* 'Evendine'	176

Preface

Most carnivorous plants stand alone in the plant world not only in their unique method of supplementary nutrition, but in the extraordinary degree to which the leaves have become changed from our idea of a typical leaf-blade to meet this end. Some have evolved into pitcher forms, often reminiscent of strange flowers, while others have developed the power of movement, reminding one in their actions of steel traps, mouse traps, or even sea anemones. The unusual to bizarre appearance of most is curious enough, but the varied and often astonishingly artful methods employed in the seduction of the prey, frequently combined with added refinements of technique which may be peculiar to a species, cannot fail to fascinate.

Carnivorous plants occur both amongst the flowering plants and in the Fungi. While some reference will be made to the principle trap types of the latter, they remain a subject in themselves, and it will be the former which concerns us here. On these, a number of works have already been published in English, mainly in the United States. While the majority of these have been brief works of a popular kind there have been some notable exceptions. *The Carnivorous Plants* by F. E. Lloyd, published as long ago as 1942, remains the classic scientific treatise on the traps themselves. Two works which must appeal to the botanist and layman alike are *The Carnivorous Plants of the United States and Canada* by Donald Schnell, and *Plants of Prey* by Rica Erickson, both dealing in detail with the species occurring in distinct geographic areas; North America and Australia respectively. Both continue to give me much pleasure, and are recommended to my readers not only as important works but for their lucid texts and beautiful illustrations. Yet up to the time of writing no work seems to have appeared in the English tongue which deals with the genera of the entire world and at the same time describes the whole plant and the structure and mechanism of its trap in detail. It is now my task to attempt to fill this void; how adequately I achieve this is entirely for the reader to judge. In so doing a problem arises, for it would be impossible to describe in this way more than a small proportion of the total species of some genera. There are, for example, more than ninety *Droseras*, and over a hundred and fifty *Utricularias*. In such cases I have tried always to select species which display the features of a distinct type, with some

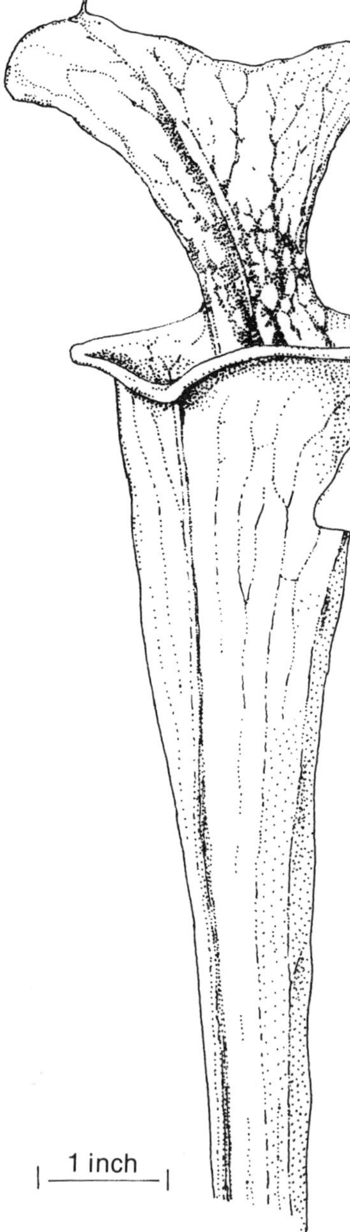

bias towards those often attractive plants which are already in cultivation and with which some of my readers may therefore become personally acquainted.

A prime consideration in planning the text has been that it should be intelligible to the layman unversed in botanical terminology. For this reason, even in describing a particular leaf or petal form, I have sought to avoid such terms where feasible. This has not always been possible, but the meanings of such exceptions are usually made obvious or may be found in the glossary. Sources of information quoted in the text may be found in the Bibliography at the end of the book.

Though this book is primarily intended as a natural history of its subject, it is becoming increasingly evident that the popularity of carnivorous plants in cultivation is steadily growing, while some few have proved adaptable to household conditions. For this reason its end part is devoted to cultural information. Though principally based upon my own experience, it incorporates the experience of many other growers, and of particular value is the contribution on growing *Heliamphora*, by Mr Joseph Mazrimas.

Quite apart from the interest provided by their traps, it should not be forgotten that the majority are attractive plants in themselves; some are indeed beautiful. Nor is this confined to the traps alone, but is seen in the flowers of most species. It may therefore seem strange that they remained largely unknown in cultivation for so long. Perhaps this was due to their being seen as plant curiosities for the botanic gardens, it somehow following that they must be difficult to cultivate while obscuring all thought of other possible virtues. Any such views are rapidly changing. There is now a growing general interest in the plants, especially evident in the United States, Britain and Japan, each of which has a Society devoted to their cultivation and study, but also in continental Europe and Australasia. A few possess an additional, more domestic appeal, as pointed out by David Hoppit in the London *Daily Telegraph*, for not only do the American Trumpet Pitchers provide an acceptable and very graceful alternative to 'ugly flypapers, swatters and sprays', but he is equally correct in asserting that the three foot high trumpets of the huge *Sarracenia flava* 'Maxima' will devour whole armies of bluebottles and wasps.

In the short period of time which has elapsed since finishing the text for the first printing some important papers have been published on recent research and discoveries. It has even been almost conclusively proved that another genus, *Triphyophyllum* (see p. 231) is carnivorous. Additionally there have been a few official changes in specific names. In the light of these and other developments the publication of a new impression provides the welcome opportunity to revise and update the work accordingly.

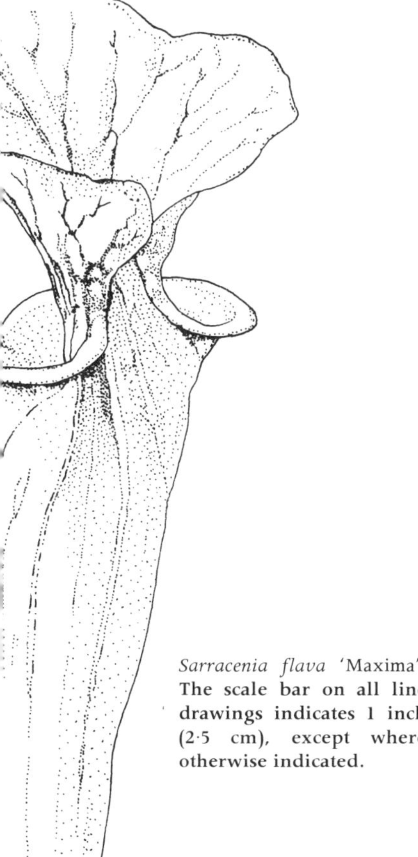

Sarracenia flava 'Maxima'. **The scale bar on all line drawings indicates 1 inch (2·5 cm), except where otherwise indicated.**

1 The Carnivorous Plants: An Introduction

It was in 1875 that Charles Darwin's well-known work *Insectivorous Plants* was first published. This provided, from the results of his own painstaking experiments, the final proof that some plants have developed the means of not only trapping small animals, but also of digesting their soft tissues and of absorbing the resulting nutrients. That was over a hundred years ago, and though the news is no longer new, first sight of a trap in action still tends to astonish those witnessing it, and continues to arouse a feeling of wonder in most of us. We tend to see plants as rightfully passive and peaceful things, very much on the opposite pole to fierce predators in the animal kingdom, and it may appear unfitting or perhaps a little unnatural that plants should have taken to themselves a role we thought reserved for the latter. Yet where it suits her Nature never hesitates to depart from what may seem the norm, and we see evidence of this in the innumerable adaptations and developments in the flowering plants, from defensive thorns, spines and prickles adapted from shoots, stalks and the teeth of leaf margins, through storage devices for food and water, as in the potato tuber and the swollen succulent stem of the cactus, to several special means of nutrition of which the carnivorous habit is but one. But in order to have a better understanding of our subject it will be advantageous first to consider briefly methods of feeding amongst the flowering plants.

The more familiar possess roots and green leaves. The roots are in the soil from which they extract all the plant's water supply which also carries mineral salts in solution containing essential food elements. The leaves also play a vital part in the plant's diet: from the air they extract carbon dioxide which they combine chemically with water to form organic compounds including carbohydrates, and more complex substances in the manufacture of which the minerals absorbed by the roots also are needed. This is achieved by the remarkable process called photosynthesis, in which the energy of sunlight is harnessed by chlorophyll, the green colouring matter in plants, which acts as the energy transformer.

Drosera aliciae leaf in the process of rolling over its prey.

The above, then, is an elementary picture of the dual methods of nutrition as they occur in most higher plants, whether they be the trees, shrubs, grasses or herbaceous plants of our gardens and countryside.

Of the special methods referred to, the most common is that known as a mycorrhizal association. This is a close association between the roots of some higher plants and the mycelia of certain fungi. The mycelium consists of a mass of thread-like filaments which feeds upon leafmould, peat or other rotting matter. Unlike fungi, higher plants cannot normally derive nourishment from such organic material, but through the mycorrhizal association they are able to obtain it indirectly via the fungus. Both parties appear to derive some benefit from the association, the fungus probably obtaining sugar and other foods from the roots of the plant. This mycorrhizal habit is found in many forest trees, which are thus able to make use of the layer of accumulated leafmould. It is also found in most heaths and heathers and in some epiphytes (plants that grow on other plants but are not parasites) and orchids. Many can in fact grow without it if so deprived (e.g. Larch, Beech, Birch and Oak), but for others, e.g. heathers, it appears essential. For the most part plants of this type possess chlorophyll, and so employ photosynthesis, but there is a small group of flowering plants—the true saprophytes—which are characterized by obtaining virtually all their food from dead, predominantly vegetable, matter through this mycorrhizal association. Examples are provided by two woodland orchids: Coral Root (*Corallorhiza*), and The Bird's Nest Orchid (*Neottia*). The leaves of true saprophytic plants do not contain chlorophyll, and so do not photosynthesize. The leaves are modified into small leafscales, often of a brownish colour.

Of rather different nature is another group: the parasitic plants. These derive all or part of their food supply from the tissues of other plants which they tap with special suckers. This is clearly not a mutually beneficial relationship but a case of plunder, for the host plant receives no recompense. The Yellow Rattle (*Rhinanthus minor*), a common grassland plant, is an example of a partial parasite, for while it obtains benefit from parasitic links formed by its roots with those of other plants, it also obtains water and salts from the soil, and the leaves are green and photosynthesize. The Broomrapes (*Orobanche*) are, on the other hand, wholly parasitic. They do not photosynthesize, and the foliage consists of brown or reddish scale-leaves devoid of chlorophyll. Some are selective, and may parasitize a particular genus only.

Lastly we come to that group of plants which is the subject of this book. We have seen how some plants extract food from rotting organic material through the agency of fungi that feed directly on it, while another group, the parasites, plunder nutriment from living plants. In a sense, carnivorous plants have something in common with both, for like the saprophytes they feed upon organic matter—in this case of animal origin—and, like the parasites, they obtain this food by plunder, albeit of the very bodies of victims which they kill. But, wonderful though the nutritional habits of saprophytes and parasites are, the carnivorous habit is not only one which we least expect in the vegetable kingdom, but one which must surprise us all in the fascinating variety of the devices in which it manifests itself. This we pp 14–17 witness in a remarkable range of traps from the simple pitfall method to others which employ movement, and in numerous means of deceiving and of luring prey. Indeed, the traps may be subject to astonishing individual adaptations, variations and refinements within a single genus, and even peculiar to a species, as we shall see amongst the Trumpet Pitchers (*Sarracenia*). That such developments are not incompatible with beauty, but rather the reverse, will be made clear by many of the photographs in this book, and it is fortunate that many plants adapt easily to cultivation.

Almost all in this group share one thing in common: they grow in soils usually of an acid, boggy, and often peaty nature in which plant foods, especially nitrogen, are deficient. Most of the exceptions seem, on the clear evidence of relationship, to descend from ancestors native to such habitats. These plants are able to make good the deficiency by catching insects and other small animals and absorbing the nutrient fluid, rich in nitrogen, resulting from their digestion. This digestive process is seen at its simplest in the Sun Pitchers (*Heliamphora*) in which it seems a mere matter of bacterial decay in the presence of rainwater caught by the pitcher, the process of decomposition releasing nutritious materials into the water which can then be gradually absorbed by the pitcher leaf. But in the majority of plants this method is either supplemented or completely replaced by the plant's own digestive system. These plants manufacture and secrete their own acids and enzymes, and the digestive process is remarkably similar to that in the stomachs of the higher animals. With the exception of the hard outer skeletons and wings of insects the entire bodies of victims are reduced by these juices to a nutritive fluid which the plant assimilates.

Examination of the remains of victims will leave little doubt of the efficiency of digestion, yet there is a mistaken belief, still supported by some writers, that the plants obtain only nitrogen from their prey. This notion seems to arise from the knowledge that not only is this element one of the most important plant foods, being a constituent of protoplasm and other vital substances, but it also happens to be particularly scarce in most of the soils in which these plants grow, so the importance of the carnivorous habit to the plant in making good this shortage is clear. But in such habitats there is also a general scarcity of other elements essential to the plant's well-being, and these too are made available in the process.

It is therefore perhaps surprising to find that most, indeed probably all carnivorous plants will survive when bereft of their diet of prey, a fact easily proved in the laboratory. Such plants lose vigour, the degree of decline no doubt depending greatly upon the quantity of nutrients available to their often limited root system, and some have been found to produce less seed. But it is very doubtful whether plants so deprived

Passive pitfalls: LEFT the Hooded Pitcher *Sarracenia minor* showing ants imbibing nectar. BELOW A tropical Pitcher Plant, *Nepenthes* x *williamsii*.

could survive for long the competition of others in their natural environments. One item of which none experience shortage in its habitat is air; all extract carbon dioxide for photosynthesis.

Passive and active traps

The various kinds of trap come in many shapes and sizes. In order to explain simply the techniques they employ I have largely followed in the footsteps of Francis Ernest Lloyd who for the same reason arranged them in order of their increasing complexity, rather than in a system of classification based on family relationship. The traps can be fundamentally divided into two groups: the *passive traps*, which, while often using ingenious methods of seducing their victims do not employ movement, and the *active traps*, which do use various movements in securing their capture or to assist in so doing.

An Introduction

RIGHT A lobster pot trap, *Sarracenia psittacina*, and BELOW a passive flypaper, *Drosophyllum lusitanicum*, with trapped fly.

Passive traps	**Active traps**
PITFALL *Heliamphora, Sarracenia, Darlingtonia, Nepenthes, Cephalotus*	FLYPAPER *Pinguicula, Drosera*
LOBSTER POT *Sarracenia psittacina, Genlisea*	STEEL TRAP *Dionaea, Aldrovanda*
FLYPAPER *Byblis, Drosophyllum*	MOUSETRAP *Utricularia, Polypompholyx*

The *Pitfall* trap, the kind found in all five genera of pitcher plants, is basically the simplest in design. The insects are attracted to the trap by means of nectar, often advertised by vivid coloration of the pitcher. Victims find their way to the richest source which is just within the

LEFT An active flypaper, the Round Leaved Sundew *Drosera rotundifolia*, with its victim. BELOW An active mousetrap, the aquatic bladderwort, *Utricularia vulgaris*.

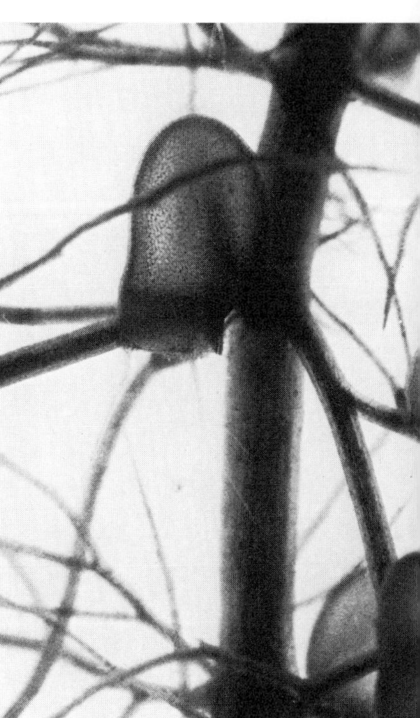

entrance. Adjoining it below is a slippery surface on to which they wander while feeding, when they suddenly lose their footing, plummeting to the bottom of the abyss beneath, from which escape is impossible.

In the *Lobster pot* trap an entry device is used through which the victim may enter, but from which it cannot find its way out. These one-way systems can be seen in the Parrot Pitcher Plant (*Sarracenia psittacina*) and in a curious aquatic, *Genlisea*, which as a trap structure different from any other.

The *Passive flypaper* is seen in the Portuguese Sundew (*Drosophyllum*) and in the Rainbow Plant (*Byblis*), which provide the only two examples. In both instances the winged victims are caught by a gluey substance secreted by the many stalked glands on the narrow linear leaves.

The *Active flypapers* comprise two genera. In the Butterwort (*Pinguicula*) the upper leaf surface is sticky with numerous tiny mucilage-secreting glands to which small insects readily adhere. When these are caught sufficiently near the margins the edges of the leaf gradually roll over them. This is too slow a movement to be of any use in overcoming the victim, but it does appear to prevent the escape

An Introduction

An active steel trap: the 'jaws' of the Venus Fly Trap *Dionaea muscipula*.

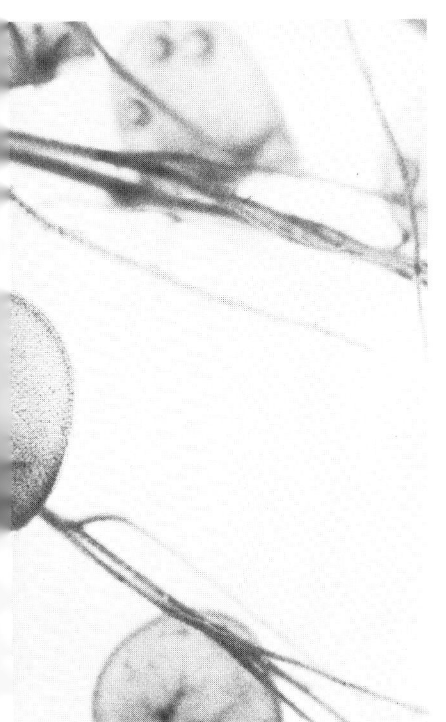

of nutritive fluid during digestion and to assist in the process itself. In the Sundew (*Drosera*), alighting insects are first caught by drops of mucilage on gland-tipped tentacles. The latter are provided with the power of movement, and what happens next will depend on what part of the leaf the victim has landed. Either it will be held in this same position, its detention assisted by other tentacles which move over to hold it, or the tentacles will bend inwards, carrying it to a central position of the leaf where other tentacles will again assist in holding it, their glands not only supplying the sticky mucilage, but being responsible for both the digestive and absorptive processes. In many species the leafblade too is capable of rolling over the victim, but as in the Butterwort this is a slow process, and seems primarily, if not solely, a means of considerably aiding digestion.

More sophisticated still is the *Steel trap* group in which we find the Venus Fly Trap (*Dionaea*) and the small aquatic Waterwheel Plant (*Aldrovanda*). The trap is formed from the leafblade, and consists of two lobes attached to a tough central vein or midrib, so that the structure is rather reminiscent of a bivalved shell-fish, and the free edge of each lobe is bordered with stiff spine-like teeth in *Dionaea*. On the inner surface of each lobe are sensitive trigger hairs. When set, the lobes are held apart, but when a creature of suitable size touches the trigger hairs two or three times the lobes close, often with extreme rapidity, seldom failing to catch their victim.

But without doubt the most remarkable trap of all is found in the aquatic and terrestrial Bladderworts (*Utricularia*). In this genus a technique comparable to that of the old fashioned mousetrap is used, for the bladder-like trap is provided with a baited trap-door complete with a tripping device. Once a small aquatic creature as much as brushes against the latter the trap is sprung—the door flies open, thus releasing a partial vacuum which sucks the victim inside, the door shuts imprisoning its prey, after which the vacuum is soon restored again and the trap is ready for further action.

The carnivorous fungi, insofar as they extend yet further the variety of vegetable traps, merit some word in passing. The fungal threads (hyphae) which form the mycelium of the aquatic fungus *Zoophagus* have short branches which attract certain species of microscopic swimming animals called rotifers, which try to feed on the ends of them. Once it is bitten, the end instantly expands, securely holding the offending rotifer by its mouth. The hold is not relinquished, and so the rotifer eventually dies. The branch then grows further into the victim's body and sends out side branches which extract the nutriment. Several fungi which prey upon eelworms use a different technique. In these, snares are formed from side branches which grow in a curve, thus uniting with the base of the hypha to form a loop. When the animal pushes its head or tail through this snare the aperture immediately contracts, holding the victim fast. In the genus *Dactylella* this is achieved by the expansion of the cells which form the loop. The animal soon dies, when its body is invaded by hyphal threads from the fungus.

Curiously, from the recent research of J. T. and C. P. Barber,[1] it appears that certain seeds with mucilaginous coverings may be capable of attracting, killing and digesting small mosquito larvae, nematodes, protozoans, and bacteria. One such seed is that of the ubiquitous Shepherd's Purse (*Capsella bursa-pastoris*). In taking up water the mucilage surrounding this seed swells, bursts through the walls and envelops the seed in a sticky coating. To this organisms adhere. As the mucilage contains the enzyme protease it seems very probable that digestion of these organisms does occur. The plants grow generally in rather poor soils, and as the seeds have low food reserves, the nutritious products of digestion thus formed around the seed would be very advantageous to the early growth of the seedling, and it is possible that the process may aid germination itself.

A question which is almost inevitably asked is, 'How, and from what peculiar leaf structure could the ancestral trap have evolved?' Unfortunately this is a question which we cannot hope to answer

[1]Superior numbers in text refer to the Bibliography, page 234

Five likely stages in the evolution of a primitive pitcher from a peltate leaf.

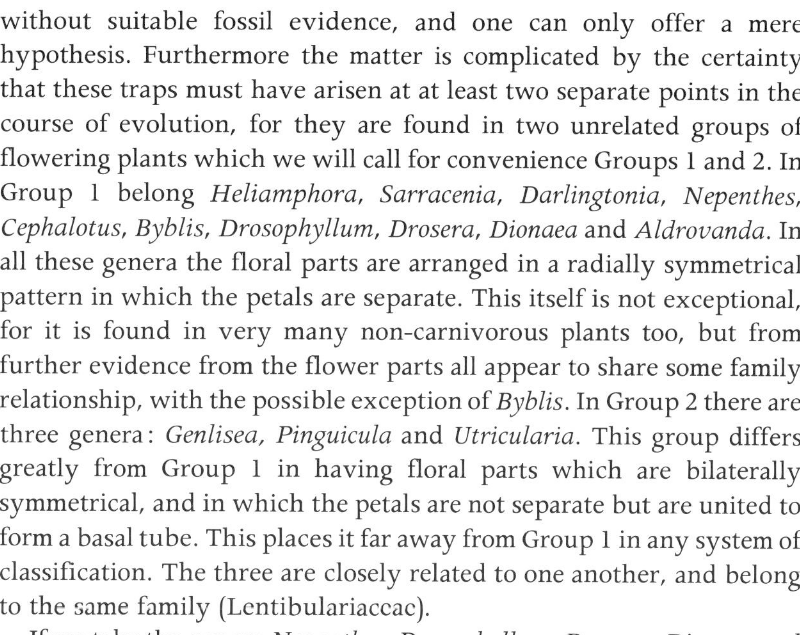

without suitable fossil evidence, and one can only offer a mere hypothesis. Furthermore the matter is complicated by the certainty that these traps must have arisen at at least two separate points in the course of evolution, for they are found in two unrelated groups of flowering plants which we will call for convenience Groups 1 and 2. In Group 1 belong *Heliamphora, Sarracenia, Darlingtonia, Nepenthes, Cephalotus, Byblis, Drosophyllum, Drosera, Dionaea* and *Aldrovanda*. In all these genera the floral parts are arranged in a radially symmetrical pattern in which the petals are separate. This itself is not exceptional, for it is found in very many non-carnivorous plants too, but from further evidence from the flower parts all appear to share some family relationship, with the possible exception of *Byblis*. In Group 2 there are three genera: *Genlisea, Pinguicula* and *Utricularia*. This group differs greatly from Group 1 in having floral parts which are bilaterally symmetrical, and in which the petals are not separate but are united to form a basal tube. This places it far away from Group 1 in any system of classification. The three are closely related to one another, and belong to the same family (Lentibulariaceae).

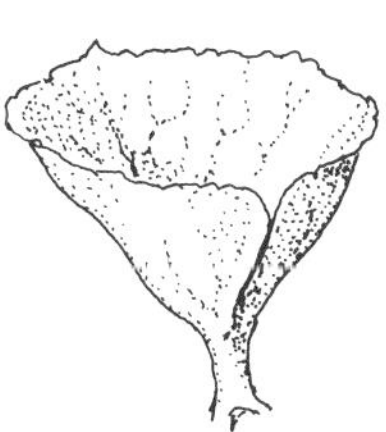

If we take the genera *Nepenthes, Drosophyllum, Drosera, Dionaea* and *Aldrovanda*, which are generally recognized to be related, two questions are valid: (a) Was their common ancestor non-carnivorous, and did their ancestral carnivorous types develop independently in two or more of the descendant lines from that ancestor, thus perhaps explaining the extraordinary differences in the types of trap? Or (b) Had this common ancestor already developed the primitive trap form from which all the present traps, however diverse in type, have evolved? We can only again speculate as to the possible answers, but on the face of it the first must seem unlikely, for taking into account the minuteness of the proportion of carnivorous genera among the flowering plants compared with those which are not, it would seem an almost impossible coincidence that two or more of these could be so related and yet possess traps which arose independently. It is true that the second suggestion may seem improbable also in the face of the complete difference of, for instance, the passive pitfall to the active flypaper, until one realizes that leaves are normally subject to far more rapid evolutionary change than are the vital parts of a flower, a fact very evident in all genera of carnivorous plants. Given gradual evolutionary change through unimaginable aeons of time there seems no reason why a sundew leaf may not evolve in countless stages from, say, a primitive pitcher leaf. The second possibility does, in the author's view, seem not only possible but probable.

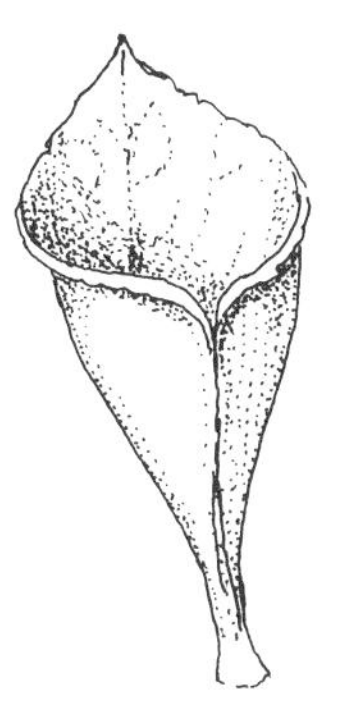

But if part or even all of Group 1 is descended from a single trap it remains for us to consider what that trap might be. It must have been very simple; ancillary prey-guiding devices must have developed later. There seem only two likely alternatives. Either it was a passive pitfall or a passive flypaper. The latter seems rather unlikely, for it is hard to

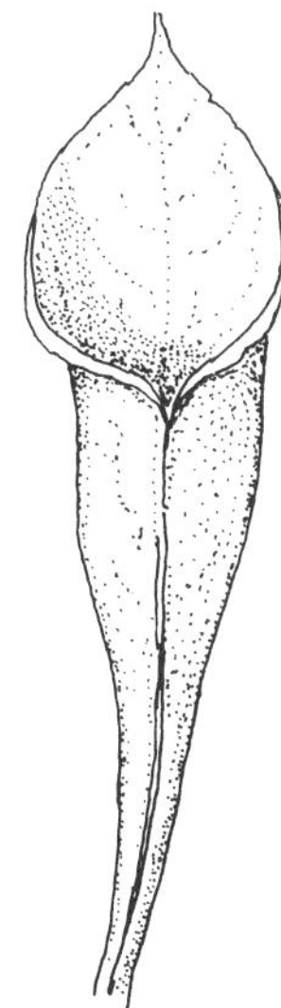

imagine how or why some of its descendants not only lost their mucilage-secreting glands on the way, but what the trap became during the long intermediary stages before evolving into a pitcher form. But it is perhaps possible, and it is easy to accept that a plant using mucilage-secreting glands as a defense system against insect marauders found by accident the means of absorbing nutriment released from the insects' bodies into the mucilage, and so became carnivorous. Yet it seems much more likely that it was a much simpler type of trap—a primitive pitcher plant. It is not difficult to imagine how this might have evolved, and this is made easier when one examines the pitcher of that most apparently primitive of the present-day pitcher plants, *Heliamphora* from South America. Structurally this pitcher appears little more than a peltate leaf (one that has a stalk attached to the middle of the undersurface) which has become rolled into a funnel form. One can without difficulty imagine the likely appearances of yet more primitive ancestors. If we start with an unremarkable peltate leaf of somewhat cupped form, sufficient to retain a little water after rainfall, insects may be expected to drown in this much as they do in any water, and their bodies will be broken down by bacterial decay so that nutrients are released into the water. We know that leaves can often absorb nutrient fluid, practical use being made of this in the modern horticultural practice of foliar feeding, and when this particular leaf absorbs some of the nutritive solution it contains we have in effect our first carnivorous plant resulting from purely accidental circumstances. This plant, with its new supplementary diet, is better equipped than some of its competitors to grow in poorer soils, and is therefore more successful. Those of its descendants with deeper 'cups' will succeed better than those in which they are shallower, due to increased capacity, and so, by the process of natural selection, the leaf will become more and more funnel-like, and can be expected to gradually evolve ancillary aids towards its carnivorous role till we have something very similar to *Heliamphora* in appearance.

In Group 2 there is less indication as to what form the primitive ancestral trap may have taken, but it may not be unreasonable to suppose that this too may have been of the pitfall type which gradually evolved into others, the pitfalls themselves becoming extinct.

2 The Pitcher Plants of Continental America

A Sun Pitcher, *Heliamphora nutans*.

The fact that the great American continent is endowed with a wider range of carnivorous genera than any other may not be in itself surprising, for its gigantic area not only spans almost every latitude from arctic regions almost to the antarctic circle, but includes a vast range of climates, altitudes and terrain. Of the fourteen genera of carnivorous plant now recognized, eight occur in the New World and of these, five are peculiar to that continent. Of these, three are pitcher plants—*Heliamphora, Sarracenia* and *Darlingtonia*—and belong to one family, Sarraceniaceae.

Despite the high degree of sophistication we see in most pitcher plants, the basic structure of the trap is very simple, and a look at the Sun Pitchers (*Heliamphora*) of South America will give a good hint as to their apparent origin, for these appear little more than flat peltate leaves rolled into the form of a funnel, though closer observation will show that the plant has developed supplementary devices to assist in attracting and overcoming the prey.

In the Trumpet Pitchers and Cobra Lily (*Sarracenia* and *Darlingtonia*) the traps have become more highly developed and often very beautiful affairs, embodying more ancillary equipment which in *Sarracenia* includes digestive glands. Yet, as we shall see, a closer study shows that they, too, are fundamentally rolled leaves, even though they have become greatly changed in appearance through the course of evolution, and it is certain that an ancestor must have been rather similar to, and closely allied with, *Heliamphora*, even though it is doubtful whether that genus would have by then evolved.

The Sun Pitchers: *Heliamphora*

Heliamphora (hel-i-*am*-fora). Fam. Sarraceniaceae
At first sight the pitchers of this South American genus may appear little more than a wide leaf rolled round and fastened in a seam just a little short of the edges, leaving the latter free to form two short wings down the front of the resulting funnel. This elementary interpretation is fairly near the truth as far as it goes, and it can certainly be said that

the Sun Pitcher is structurally the most primitive of all pitcher plants. There seems something inexpressibly strange about these traps: living likenesses, one may presume, of a race of primeval types, now long extinct, which must have enjoyed wide ranges of distribution during their heyday, it is almost as if one was able to view a brontosaurus face to face. But the Sun Pitchers are of very restricted occurrence indeed, and are isolated upon a few mountains which are so remote and of such difficult access that few civilized men have been there. Indeed much of this area of highland, largely made up of the Sierra Pacaraima in the extreme south of Venezuela, remained uncharted until recently. Situated between the great Orinoco river on its north and the humid forests of the wide Amazon basin to its south, it experiences one of the highest rainfalls in the world. From all accounts it is a singular place. The mountains are for the most part flat-topped with vertical sides. This has often resulted in the near or complete isolation of many plants and animals to single table mountains, causing separate evolution on separate mountains, which has resulted in many species and numerous varieties peculiar to one or two mountains. This is well illustrated in the Sun Pitchers, in which three of the six species appear to be entirely separated from others in this way.

A young plant of *Heliamphora nutans*, natural size.

The drenching conditions in this region have resulted in the formation of numerous streams and bogs, and it is in the latter that the Sun Pitchers abound. It was as long ago as 1839 that the first species to be discovered, *Heliamphora nutans*, was collected by Sir Robert Schomburgk in 'a marshy savannah, at an elevation of six thousand feet on Mount Roraima'. Its generic name comes from the Greek *helos*, a marsh, and *amphora*, a pitcher, later confusion with *helios*, the sun, having led to its common name. For some ninety years this was the only species known, then *H. tatei* was discovered, and *H. minor*, *H. heterodoxa*, *H. ionasi* and *H. neblinae* have since been added to the list.

The trap

Though the length of pitcher varies amongst species from $2\frac{1}{4}$ to over 14 inches (5·5–35 cm), the basic structure remains very similar. The funnel gradually widens from the base upwards for the greater part of its length, then after a neck-like constriction which is hardly noticeable in some species, the tube expands into an elliptical bell. This ellipse results from the manner in which the edges of the bell rise sharply from the front to the rear where they nearly terminate in a point, which is, however, crowned by a short erect stalk bearing a tiny spoon-like structure which represents the apex of the leaf. To the front of the bell the margins either fuse together immediately, or continue in a slit down the front of the pitcher before joining. Very shortly below this union, the edges expand outwards to form two keel-like wings, and these are continued downwards to the base. The opened pitchers soon fill with rainwater as far as the slit, or, where this is absent, to the front margin

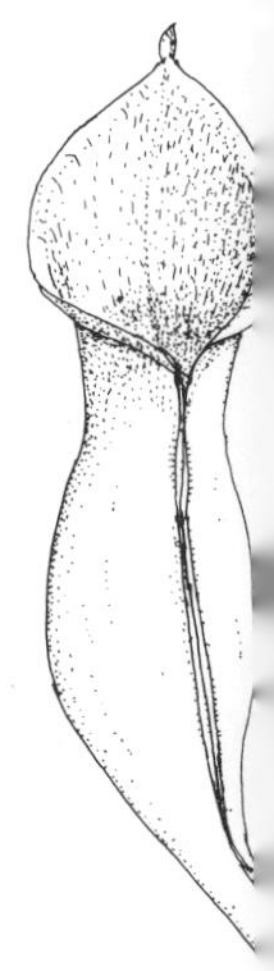

Heliamphora pitcher: trap structure.

of the bell. The slit effectively prevents the escape or loss of prey, while allowing the escape of excess water which might otherwise render the pitcher top heavy. In the taller-pitchered species there is often also a small pore lower down the front of the pitcher which acts as an additional overflow.

The internal surface of the pitcher is in four distinct zones. The first is the spoon, which is clearly a device for beguiling prey, for its smooth concave surface is liberally scattered with nectar-secreting glands. The structure is often slightly inclined forwards, which must assist in protecting nectar from the leaching effect of rain. The second zone includes the entire bell, extending also a little distance below. It, too, is dotted with nectar glands attractive to insects, but is also covered with a thick coating of downward-pointing hairs. The latter are of somewhat different structure and function to those we shall see in the hoods of the Trumpet Pitcher (*Sarracenia*), for they offer an uncertain foothold to their potential victims which, in their efforts to obtain the nectar from the glands beneath are likely to slip, so falling downwards into the waterbath beneath. The third zone is smooth and highly polished, offering little chance of a foothold. The fourth and last zone is armed with short, sharp, downward-pointing hairs whose sole function appears to be that of retaining captured prey. The pitcher is totally devoid of digestive glands, and the plants seem to rely entirely upon bacteria to break down the bodies of their victims. The nutritive substances released by this process of bacterial decay dissolve in the water, and the pitcher is able readily to absorb this solution.

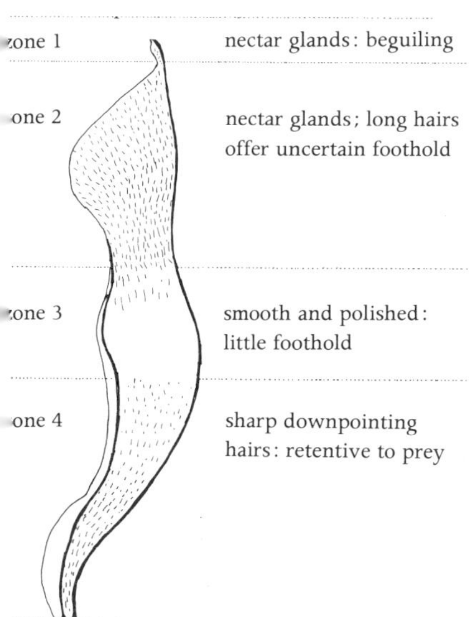

The flowers

There are several flowers to a scape, or stalk. These are nodding and delicately pretty, white at first, later turning to pink. They hang from long pedicels, each of which is clasped by an elliptical bract where it arises from the stem. There are no petals; what appear to be these are in fact sepals, of which there are four, or rarely five or six. These are oval, tapering to a pronounced point. The simple pistil is straight and central, and is surrounded by eight or more stamens. The scapes are often of a reddish colour contrasting well with the white flowers, and are up to 16 inches (40 cm) tall in those species at present in cultivation. It is possible that they may be taller in other species, of which we have at present insufficient information.

The species

The first three described are in cultivation. All three have similar pitcher coloration. The margins of the pitchers are reddish, especially around their openings, and parallel veins become conspicuously red down their outsides. The cap, as the spoon-like structure is properly termed, is always reddish inside. The other species differ markedly.

Heliamphora

Heliamphora minor This is the smallest known. The pitchers generally range from $2\frac{1}{4}$ to 3 inches (5·5–7·5 cm) in height, and from $\frac{1}{3}$ to $\frac{3}{8}$ inch (8 mm–1 cm) in diameter. Its cap is the smallest of the three. It occurs on Mount Auyan-Tepui, Venezuela. Discovered by Dr G. H. H. Tate in 1937.

Heliamphora nutans Pitchers from 4 to 6 inches (10–15 cm) long, $\frac{3}{4}$ to $1\frac{1}{4}$ inches (2–3 cm) in diameter. Found on Mount Roraima, Venezuela.

Heliamphora heterodoxa The pitchers range from 6 to 10 inches (15–25 cm) in length, and are $1\frac{1}{4}$ to 2 inches (2–5 cm) in diameter. Its cap is the largest found in these three species. It occurs on Mount Ptari-Tepui, Venezuela. Discovered, and named in 1951 by Dr Julian Steyermark.

Heliamphora tatei var. *tatei* Discovered in 1928 by Dr G. H. H. Tate on Mount Duida, Venezuela, this is a remarkable plant as, alone in its family it forms shrubby stems. These may approach a height of 5 feet (1·5 m) or more on the moor-like savannahs it especially favours, scrambling to as much as 13 feet (4 m) in light woodland. The pitchers are much elongated, especially in the bell which is tubular, only flaring at the margin, and the rise of gradient of the edges from the front to back of the bell is less marked than in the species already described, while the caps tend to be larger with wider supporting columns. Some distance below the frontal slit is a drainage pore. A variety, *H. tatei* var. *macdonaldiae*, until recently regarded as a separate species, differs only in that the inner surface of the bell is almost entirely devoid of hairs except along the margin in the lower part of the neck. The former *H. tyleri* is now considered too similar to *H. tatei* var. *tatei* to even merit separate varietal status.

Heliamphora ionasi Discovered in 1952 by Bassett Maguire and Jonah Boyan on Ilu-tepui, Venezuela, this produces the most impressive pitchers of the genus, sometimes exceeding 18 inches (46 cm) in height, and possessing widely flared bells surmounted by rather large caps. Their upper parts often become pink to reddish with age. They were found on and beneath the topmost cliff faces of the mountain, forming often gigantic rosettes.

Heliamphora neblinae This species was discovered by Maguire, Wurdack and Bunting in 1953 on the Cerro de la Neblina, Venezuela. The bell is rather narrow and very long, usually equalling the length of the lower part of the pitcher. The rise of gradient of the rim from front to back is very slight, and the rim is only slightly reflexed. In proportion to the pitcher size, the cap is the largest known. There are three varieties: *H. neblinae* var. *neblinae*, with white flowers, var. *viridis* with greenish flowers, and var. *parva* with shorter pitchers tinged with red, and white sepals tipped with pale pink.

The Trumpet Pitchers: Sarracenia

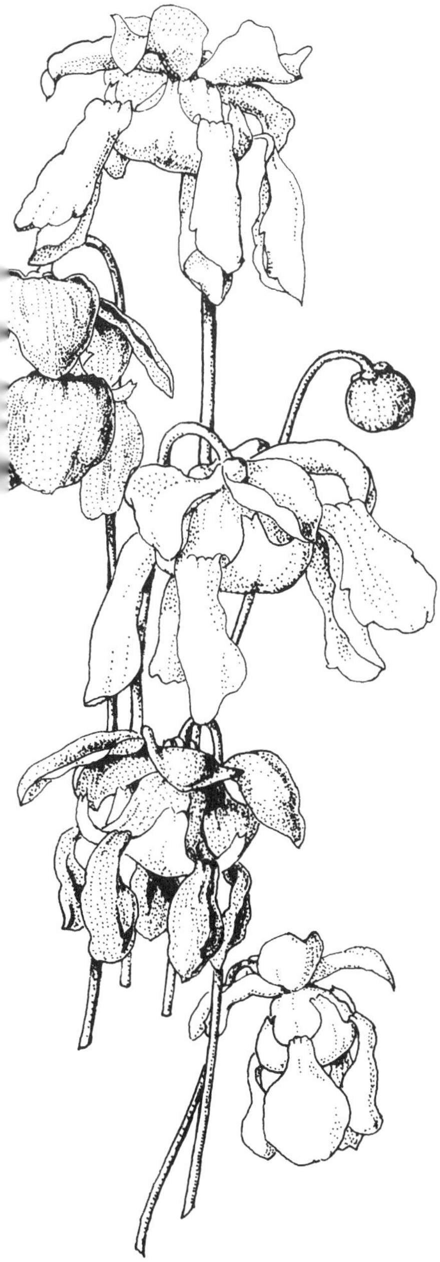

Sarracenia (sarras-see-neea). Fam. Sarraceniaceae
The wide variations in the basic pitfall trapping technique found amongst the species in this genus manifest themselves in an equal variety of pitcher form. In the basic type the leaf is moulded into a long upright funnel-shaped tube which is surmounted at its rear by a lid-like but immobile structure commonly termed the hood. Amongst the species of this kind are found some of the most attractive of all carnivorous plants, for they combine graceful and often magnificently variegated foliage with great beauty of flower. The unexpected supplementary adaptations of others cannot fail to fascinate, rather more from the sheer subtlety of their individual mechanisms than from the distinctly bizarre form of their pitchers. Some degree of colour variegation is displayed in most species. This is usually seen as red or maroon veins in the upper pitcher and hood. Venation may be sparing and simply branched, finely netted, or it can be heavy, extending over most of the outer pitcher surface, and in some species the entire pitcher may become brilliantly suffused with dark red. In some forms of the White Trumpet (*S. leucophylla*) the upper pitcher and hood are pure white netted with dark red, often with some pink suffusion creeping from the red veins into the white areas between, while white translucent 'windows' or false exits are a conspicuous part of the upper pitchers in both the Hooded and Parrot Pitcher Plants (*S. minor* and *S. psittacina*).

Particularly lovely are the nodding solitary flowers which burst from large globular terminal buds on tall upright stems. They may exceed 3 inches (7·5 cm) in diameter in some forms, and consist of five petal-like sepals under which hang the five rather longer true petals which overhang the curious pistil. The latter is of its kind unique, and very much resembles an inverted umbrella. It is five-lobed, and is supported on a narrow column which arises centrally from the round five-celled ovary. Each lobe is notched at its apex, and at the base of this notch is the tiny stigma. The colour of the petals ranges from palest brimstone through pink to deepest garnet-crimson, while the sepals are often of a rather deeper shade, sometimes tinged with mahogany. The umbrella-like pistil may be a creamy white, sometimes tinted with the colour of the petals, or it may be pale to mid-green.

Sarracenia flowers. From the top: *S. flava, S. purpurea, S. flava, S. leucophylla, S. minor*. See also pages 33 and 175.

Sarracenia

The *Sarracenia* flower. LEFT a dissected flower to show floral parts. BELOW A: diagrammatic cross-section and B: the stigmas and position of the petal between pistil lobes.

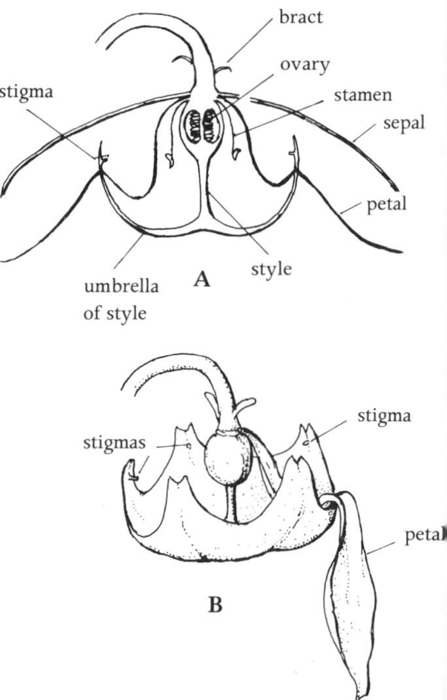

When the pollen is ripe, it is shed on to the saucer-like floor of the umbrella where it can be involuntarily picked up on the bodies of insects, principally bees, visiting the flower for its nectar. From the interior the most obvious exit for the creature is at the base of the U-like curve between two pistil lobes, for the petal which forms a curtain in front of this may be pushed outwards by the visitor without difficulty. In this way the insect does not come in contact with the stigma, so that self-fertilization of the flower is avoided. But this would prove an almost impossible way by which to *enter* a flower, since the petal cannot be pushed inwards because the umbrella is in the way. The entry the insect chooses is down the interior surface of one of the five pistil lobes, each of which is exposed to view between the petals. By this route, some pollen sticking to the body of the insect from a previously-visited flower is likely to be brushed off against the stigma, and in this way cross-pollination is effected.

The first known record of any species is a drawing of the Hooded Pitcher Plant of around 1576, though there can be little doubt that *S. purpurea*, the Huntsman's Cup, must have been familiar to many of the earliest settlers on the eastern seaboard long before that time. Yet it is curious that no record of the latter species has been found prior to a drawing by Clusius of 1601.

In that engaging work *Travels in North and South Carolina, Georgia, and Florida*, which he wrote in 1793, William Bartram enthusiastically describes the beauties of *Sarracenia* species in flower in the wild, and of the curious structure of their pitchers. He was in no doubt that the latter are constructed so as to catch large quantities of insects, even surmising, as we now know correctly, that the short, stiff, downpointing hairs within serve to prevent the victims from making their escape. It therefore seems odd that he doubted whether 'the insects caught in the leaves, and which dissolve and mix with the fluid, serve for aliment or support', suspecting rather that the fluid in the pitchers was a provision against drought. Yet from this very statement it is clear that he had at

Sarracenia flava. *Sarracenia* seed heads retain all floral parts except the petals and stamens. At the foot of the picture can be seen flattened leaf-like structures called phyllodia, predominantly derived from modified leaf stalks.

least considered the possibility of carnivory, and he may have been the first to do so. Little more thought seems to have been given to the subject until the second half of the nineteenth century, when the possibility that the genus was carnivorous became increasingly suspected. Darwin himself conducted no research on these plants, but in his *Insectivorous Plants* of 1875 notes that 'from the excellent observations' of two American physicians and amateur botanists, Doctors Joseph H. Mellichamp and W. M. Canby, 'there can scarcely be a doubt that *Sarracenia* and *Darlingtonia* may be added to this class, though the fact can hardly be considered as yet fully proved.' That final proof came some twelve years later, when experiments conducted by the same Dr Mellichamp provided conclusive evidence that the bodies of animals caught by the pitchers are both digested and absorbed.

There are eight generally recognized species in the genus, though there is some debate as to whether two plants usually considered as subspecies of *S. rubra*, ssp. *jonesii* and ssp. *alabamensis*, should be given specific rank. The majority are found in the south-eastern states of the United States, principally on the coastal plains, but the northern subspecies of *S. purpurea*, ssp. *purpurea*, ranges as far north as the arctic regions of Canada. p. 45

Both the species and hybrids make excellent subjects for cultivation. Quite apart from their interest as carnivores, their flowers are often large, in rich but subtle colours, and sometimes possess a pleasant fragrance. The stems are long and straight, the flowers last well in water, and are therefore excellent as cut flowers. But the attractions of the plants extend far beyond the flowering period, for the pitchers vie with the blooms themselves in beauty of form and richness of colour variegation. Nor is this all, for many very amply repay the little attention they require in the safe control of houseflies. *S. flava* will be found to be especially efficient, while its form 'Maxima' doubles rather well as a wasp trap. Once considered botanical curiosities, and therefore 'difficult', the majority are on the contrary extremely easy to grow once their simple requirements are understood. That they may be grown successfully both in the greenhouse and home, and occasionally even out of doors is explained in detail in the latter part of this book.

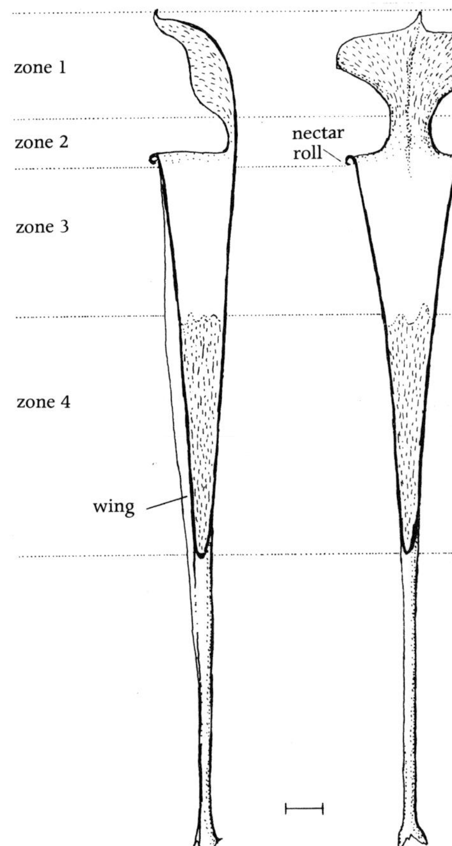

The trap

In describing the typical pitcher it will be well to take as our example the upright, trumpet-shaped kind which we find in the species *flava, oreophila, alata* and *rubra*, for these display basic features which are modified in one way or another in other species. The most obvious external feature is the trumpet-like tube. This is surmounted at its back by the lid-like hood, which is supported on a short stem, the column. The mouth, where not interrupted by the hood, has a rounded rim termed the nectar roll. A flat keel-like structure, the wing, runs down the front of the pitcher from the bottom of the nectar roll to within a short distance of the base. Though the close relationship of *Sarracenia* and *Heliamphora* cannot be doubted, dissimilarities in the pitchers of the two genera are at once apparent. Where in *Heliamphora* the end of the leaf stands free, forming the open 'bell', in *Sarracenia* this same area is divided into two parts. Of these, the upper is equivalent to the back region of the bell in *Heliamphora*, and is here seen as the beautifully formed and lid-like hood, while what would have been the sides and front of the bell have been rolled outwards and modified in *Sarracenia* to form the nectar roll. The single frontal wing that we see in *Sarracenia* represents nothing less than the fusion of twin primeval wings which, as in those of *Heliamphora*, represented in an ancestral type the free margins of the primitive leaf projecting beyond the 'seam' of the pitcher. In these ways alone *Sarracenia* shows considerable evolutionary advancement on its cousin. The entire external surface of the pitcher is dotted with nectar glands. These become more numerous towards the top of the pitcher and are particularly abundant on the wing.

The interior of the pitcher is divided down its length into several distinct zones with rather different functions. The Victorian botanist Sir Joseph D. Hooker seems to have been the first to draw attention to these, and recognized four in *S. purpurea* to which F. E. Lloyd has added a fifth. They are clearly defined in some species (e.g. *S. purpurea*), while in others two zones may merge gradually or overlap; however their order of arrangement and functions remain pretty much the same in all species. We here take the pitcher of *S. flava*.

Zone 1 in this species includes more or less the whole interior surface of the hood, with the exception of the lowest part of the column. The surface is scattered with nectar glands, and interspersed between these are short, sharp, downward-pointing hairs. Zone 2 lies immediately beneath this. It includes the lower part of the column, all the nectar roll, and all the internal surface of the mouth to an approximate depth of $\frac{1}{3}$ inch (8 mm). The nectar-secreting glands are very numerous, and are so abundant on the nectar roll and on the back of the pitcher just beneath the base of the column that these surfaces are often visibly wet. Insects standing on this zone are offered very little foothold. In this species Zone 2 merges gradually into Zone 3. Zone 3 extends for several inches down the tube. It has a glossy waxy surface which offers no foothold to insects. Its surface is scattered with microscopic glands, very similar to the nectar glands of the zones above, but in this case secreting juices containing digestive enzymes. This is followed by Zone 4, which reaches to the bottom of the tube, and is lined with long, sharp, downward-pointing hairs. In this zone the surface cells lack the waterproof waxy surface known as cuticle which normally covers the exposed face of epidermal cells.

The scent of nectar is sufficiently attractive in itself to tempt insects

nectar glands and short pointed hairs: sure foothold

nectar glands numerous: slippery

glands secrete digestive enzymes: no foothold

no cuticle; long downward pointed hairs

Sarracenia flava: trap structure.

from some distance away, but its presence is further advertised in most species and forms by the gradual development of colour in the opened pitcher. This usually displays itself as crimson or maroon veins in the upper part of the pitcher and hood, but the pitcher itself frequently becomes tinted with red or yellow, while in *S. leucophylla* the tops may be white, often veined in red and suffused with pink.

p. 34

The pitchers attract both crawling and flying insects. The former consist mainly of ants, which seem to especially favour *S. rubra* and *S. minor*. The most popular thoroughfare for these is the generously nectared wing. Winged visitors may alight on any part of the pitcher, since nectar is available over the entire exterior, though the lid is the most popular landing ground. Those that settle on the tube tend to ascend it, and this is probably largely explained by the increasing supplies of nectar thus encountered, though the coloured veins no doubt assist in providing nectar guides to the richest sources, just as is the case in the coloured veins of many petals. Thus, most of these visitors tend to find their way to the nectar roll in Zone 2. Similarly, insects on the hood are encouraged down to the same zone, where they encounter the rich supplies in the vicinity of the base of the column. It has been often said that they are further urged in that direction by the sharp downpointing hairs with which the interior surface of the hood is covered, but though this may be true in the case of very small creatures, the majority of visitors appear to experience no more difficulty in ascending than in descending this surface.

Sarracenia flava. The nectar trail around the edge of the outer hood is rich, leading down to even richer supplies in the danger area of the throat.

Once an insect has found its way to the superabundant food source in Zone 2 the slippery surface places it in very grave danger, for as it paces the area it is almost certain to lose its footing. When this occurs it may plunge helplessly into the depths below, or it may find its wings in time and fly to safety. If so, it seldom seems particularly dismayed by its experience, and often repeats the action several times, when its luck may run out. Flying, however, is difficult in such restricted space, and many insects will fail to clear the sides. If so, no grip is offered by the waxy walls of Zone 3 which merely act as a slide, precipitating the victim into Zone 4 beneath. Here, the long downpointing hairs impede ascent but encourage descent, and the victim's prospects of escape are not made any brighter by the fact that the wings and entire body are often clogged by the fluid secreted by the glands in Zone 3 which accumulates in the base of the pitcher. Once the victim is in Zone 4 its fate is sealed; it cannot escape and will soon die.*

After the death of the insect digestion begins, and continues until all the soft parts of the creature are dissolved and all that is left is its hard chitinous exterior or skeleton and the wings. In *Sarracenia* it is usually a combined process involving bacterial decay and the action of acids and enzymes secreted by the digestive glands in Zone 3. The enzymes invertase and protease are present, and also perhaps amylase and lipase, capable of breaking down proteins, starches and fats, respectively.

*Some observers, the author included, have noted that many victims are overcome while apparently intoxicated, in which state they are easy victims for the pitfall. Recent research has in fact isolated the insect paralysing agent coniine in the volatile constituents of the pitcher of *S. flava.* (See bibliography: N. V. Mody et al, *Specialia*, 32, part 7.)

Bacteria are not found in the unopened pitcher, but are introduced afterwards, mainly upon the bodies of the victims themselves. Given bacteria-free conditions, the digestive juices alone are capable of breaking down animal bodies. Conversely, so are bacteria alone, but the combined process is altogether faster and more efficient. In their dissolved state the nutritive substances are easily assimilated by the pitcher. This process takes place in the bottom part of the tube, Zone 4, where it will be remembered that the surface cells have no covering of waterproof cuticle. Consequently there is nothing to prevent the transference of the nutritive solution into the sap of these epidermal cells by the process known as diffusion, and thus into the plant's system.

Once the soft parts of the victims' bodies are digested, the remaining skeletons become rather fragile in the absence of supporting tissue. As the pitcher fills, these husks become crushed and compacted by the weight of the bodies above, and this is easily observable if a well-filled pitcher of *S. flava* is cut longitudinally at the end of the season. In this way a large trap of this species is fully capable of catching many thousands of insects during its lifetime.

The species

Much variety of form and coloration is to be found in the pitchers of the different species in this genus. This is even evident in those that overcome their prey by the simple pitfall method, which we have discussed. Other species have, however, developed supplementary and highly individualistic techniques of tricking and capturing insects, and employ devices as various as a waterbath, window-like false exits, and an 'eeltrap'. As explained earlier, I will describe the species according to the trap type, starting with the simplest.

The Basic Pitfall

THE YELLOW TRUMPET *Sarracenia flava* This elegant species is one of the simplest to please in cultivation, and is amongst the best known. In Britain it is becoming increasingly popular for providing a decorative yet often efficient means of controlling the common housefly. Its range extends from south Alabama through northern Florida and south Georgia, continuing through the coastal plain areas of the Carolinas into south-west Virginia.

So conspicuous a plant must have attracted the attention of settlers a century earlier, yet the first botanist to describe it appears to have been the naturalist Mark Catesby in 1731. He named it *Sarracenia foliis longioribus et angustioribus*, an alarming mouthful, but this was six years before Linnaeus was to revolutionize the classification and nomenclature of plants with the publication of his *Species Plantarum*. By 1752 it was in cultivation in Europe.

The pitchers are tall and erect. The tube is trumpet-like, widening gradually upwards and flaring at the mouth much like the bell of a clarinet. The frontal wing is never very wide, seldom exceeding $\frac{1}{8}$ inch (3 mm), and is often reduced to a mere rib towards the top where it joins the nectar roll. The latter is more or less horizontal, except to the front where it tends to dip forward, rather suggesting the short spout of a jug. The column of the hood ascends steeply, and is slightly inclined inwards. Its margins are reflexed, and down its centre is a pronounced furrow which continues downwards into the tube for a little distance and for a shorter distance upwards into the lid, in both cases diminishing in depth as it goes. From the column the lid portion of the hood expands. It ascends at a rather lower angle than the column, and overhangs the mouth of the pitcher which it exceeds in diameter. It is more or less circular, but terminates in a point which is drawn out at its end into an erect spur. The latter represents the apex or terminating point of the midrib, or central leaf vein, which runs up the back of the pitcher into the hood. The margins of the lid are slightly reflexed.

pp. 8–9

A good deal of variation is found in this species where it occurs on the Atlantic coastal plain, especially evident in the pitcher coloration, form and stature. Exposed to sunlight it usually changes from pale green to greenish yellow or almost pure golden yellow. There is a touch of dark red within the column, from which a few red veins emerge for a very limited distance. In other forms the outer surface of the hood and sometimes the outer surface of the upper tube also are suffused with a fine copper red. In many others the inside of the hood and the inner and outer surfaces of the upper tube are finely veined in maroon, while in some this coloured venation may be so heavy that the maroon colour predominates. Distinctly different forms are found growing side by side. In height the pitchers are usually between 20 and 30 inches (51–76 cm), but in some forms they may not exceed 18 inches (46 cm), whilst in others they may reach 1 yard (90 cm). Far less variation is seen amongst the populations on the Gulf Coast. The pitchers here are generally taller and more robust than those on the eastern coastal plain. There is commonly a red blotch of colour on the column, but no red venation elsewhere. Mr Paul McMillan suggests that, as large and consistent populations occupy the area in which it occurs, it should be considered as a distinct variety, and suggests the use of the name once given to it, *S. flava* var. *rugelii*.[2]

By the late summer pitcher production has normally ceased, and another leaf-like structure is produced in their place. This is like a leaf both in its form and in its function—flat, rather thick, and somewhat resembling an iris leaf. It is not in fact a true leaf at all, but is thought to to be a flattened petiole, or leafstalk. The pitchers die back during late autumn and early winter, but these phyllodia as they are called (sing. phyllode) remain green, persisting long after the new pitchers are formed the following spring.

p. 27

Pitchers and yellow flowers of *Sarracenia flava*, and the brick red flowers of the hybrid *Sarracenia* x *catesbaei*.

The flowers are amongst the finest, and certainly the largest in this

genus. They are borne on tall stems, and open while the pitchers are still in early growth. The petals are of a clear yellow, the sepals of a rather deeper tone, while the pistil is light green. The blooms differ somewhat in size, generally according to the stature of the plant, the sepal span ranging from about 2½ to 4 inches (6·5–10 cm). There is a slight, rather bitter-sweet fragrance.

THE GREEN PITCHER PLANT *Sarracenia oreophila* This rare species from the Appalachian mountains was for long considered a form or variant of the Yellow Trumpet. Though it does bear a superficial resemblance to *S. flava* there are very distinct dissimilarities. It was first collected by Dr H. M. Neisler in 1875, who found it growing in Taylor County, Georgia. He recognized these differences, and sent specimens to the botanists Asa Gray and John Torrey. They, however, attached insufficient importance to them, and identified the plants as *S. flava*. So the confusion remained until 1933, when it was described by Dr Edgar T. Wherry, who pointed out the distinctions, at the same time recognizing it as a species.

p. 36

The pitcher is usually rather shorter than in *S. flava*, and is generally of a pale green which often becomes tinted rosy red with age, especially in its upper parts. Forms occur with finely netted red venation in the upper tube and hood. As in *S. flava*, the mouth is wide and flaring, but it tends to be rather rounder, often forming a nearly perfect semi-circle. The lip tends to be on one level, lacking the low frontal 'spout' of *S. flava*, and the nectar roll is of a more uniform thickness. But perhaps the most noticeable difference is in the hood, which is set at a more erect angle than in *S. flava*. The column itself is almost vertical, is less reflexed towards its edges, and is often rather narrower than in *S. flava*, while the margins of the lid are hardly reflexed at all.

Around midsummer these pitchers start to die down in nature (this is not always so in cultivated plants). In their place the plant sends up phyllodia, which persist till the following spring when new pitchers are again produced. D. E. Schnell, when observing plants on the Sand Mountain Plateau, noted that the pitcher die-back coincides with a seasonal advent of hot weather and a decreased rainfall, at which time there is considerable drying out of the ground in which they grow. The dying of the pitchers would seem to be a convenient means of overcoming this annual situation. The phyllodia provide a convenient means of distinguishing the species from *S. flava*, for they are not only shorter, but their upper half is bent sideways to form a sickle shape, while in *S. flava* they are almost straight. The flowers, too, are distinct. Similar to those of *S. flava* in form, they differ in colour, being a yellowish green, and they possess a distinctly sweet fragrance.

This is essentially a mountain plant, favouring habitats rather different from those associated with other species. The ground is usually marshy rather than truly boggy, and the plants are often found

Red veining on the lid and throat of *S. leucophylla* attracts the flies. Downward-pointing-hairs may encourage the prey into the trap.

in wet places at the side of streams, or by ponds. The soil may vary from sandy clay often associated with rocks, to peat. So dry may this become during the summer heat that no other species in the genus could be expected to survive such conditions in the long term. Its range must have been restricted even before the coming of the first European settlers, but its existence as a wild plant is now increasingly endangered by agriculture, land-drainage and afforestation, and, regrettably, by the activities of unscrupulous collectors. Now entirely extinct in Georgia where Neisler first discovered it, it is found in only a limited—and declining—number of stations in north-east Alabama. It is plain that unless firm action is soon taken to thoroughly protect a number of these stands, the species is destined for early extinction in the wild; a serious loss to the world's flora which could and should be avoided if appropriate steps are taken by the right authorities in time.

Due to its widely differing environmental preferences the range of this species is entirely isolated from those of others except at one point. This is near the town of Birmingham, Alabama, where it occurs together with *S. rubra*.

p. 34

THE WHITE TRUMPET *Sarracenia leucophylla* This, with its flower-like pitchers which are often variegated in white, crimson and pink, and its deep ruby-red flowers, is surely one of the most beautiful plants of the wet savannahs in which it grows. Its range extends from north-west Florida into south-west Georgia and from thence westwards through the extreme south of Alabama to just over the Mississippi border. Probably first discovered by William Bartram, his description of the plant was partly confused with another species. It was next described by the botanist Constantine Samuel Rafinesque who named it *S. leucophylla*. This is now the accepted name, though until recently it was almost universally known as *S. drummondii*.

The pitchers are tall, slender and erect. They are usually about 30 inches (75 cm) high, but may exceed 1 yard (90 cm). The wing is rather undeveloped and the tube is slim and green for the greater part of its length, but towards the mouth it widens into a bell which is simply flared in some forms, while in others it narrows slightly at the rim to give a rather inflated, belly-like appearance to the widest part immediately below. The nectar roll usually slopes slightly downwards towards the front where it dips to form a spout, as in *S. flava*. The bell is most beautifully and richly variegated, even between plants within a single stand. Pure white is usually dominant, and this is usually conspicuously mullioned with a network of veins. These often rapidly change from green to brownish green to a brilliant crimson-red, and frequently this colour suffuses into parts of the white areas which become flushed with a delicate rose pink. In other plants these veins may remain green, or turn through chocolate to pure maroon, while occasionally the green or coloured veins are so sparse or narrow as to

Sarracenia oreophila

give the impression that the tops are purely white. This variegation is continued on the hood, where it is at its most brilliant on the back. The column of the hood is rather wide, and occupies a third of the circumference of the mouth. It merges immediately with the lid, which is rather large, and overhangs the mouth at an angle of some forty-five degrees. The marginal areas of the latter are reflexed, and undulate along the edges. The midrib is seen as a pronounced central keel-like rib on the back of the lid which terminates in a spur at the apex which is hook-like and backward-pointing.

The lovely flowers possess a sweet fragrance. They are borne on long slender stems which are rather taller than the spring pitchers with which they sometimes open simultaneously. The petals are of a rich and intense red verging upon ruby, the sepals are of still darker tone suffused with mahogany, while the pistil is of deep copper. p. 25

Writers of the late nineteenth and early twentieth centuries sometimes refer to a number of named varieties of the species which might appear to have passed out of cultivation since that time. This would seem a pity until one realizes how variable this plant is in the wild. Plants which appear to exactly answer the descriptions of these varieties occur in nature, a fact well borne out by the following account of a field visit written by Mr Robert C. Folkerts. Speaking of a large stand in Mississippi, he recalls: 'most notable to me at first, aside from the sheer beauty of these plants, was their remarkable diversification of coloration and pattern even within single colony groupings. Many lids were predominantly white with almost no venation or red coloration, some had mostly red venation, while still others had both red and green patterns. At least one specimen had a snow-white cap with a red border around the edge. Variation within *leucophylla* species seemed almost endless, and it set me wondering how many genetic combinations could ever be clearly separated into one classification . . . one specimen of about average height . . . had a remarkably large opening, almost three inches across.' He adds that 'great efficiency of insect trapping mechanisms became apparent because so many of the pitchers were literally bursting at the seams with insect carcases.'[3] An efficiency, one may add, which is equally apparent in cultivated plants. Hover-flies are attracted to this species more than to any other, and the flower-like appearance of the pitcher may play a leading role in their allurement.

THE PALE PITCHER PLANT *Sarracenia alata* This species occurs on the eastern plain of Texas, and is the only *Sarracenia* endemic to that State. From there its range extends through the southern half of Louisiana and the extreme south of Mississippi over the border into the most south-westerly corner of Alabama.

The plant was confused with *S. flava* in the nineteenth century, and later with *S.* x *catesbaei*. That it should have been confounded with the latter, a natural hybrid and of very different appearance, must seem p. 33

Sarracenia alata

extraordinary, but at that time *S.* x *catesbaei* was still regarded as a species, and its identity had been erroneously associated with the plant we now know as *S. alata* due to a mistake in the identification of some herbarium material. This came to light in 1904, when J. M. Macfarlane found that these specimens, collected by the botanist S. Elliott as *S. catesbaei*, were nothing of the kind. They were in fact what appeared to be an as yet undescribed species, to which he gave the name of *S. sledgei* after a Dr W. H. Sledge of Mobile, but which is now correctly termed *S. alata*. He also found that the true *S.* x *catesbaei* was not a species at all, but a natural hybrid of rather frequent occurrence, *S. flava* x *S. purpurea venosa*.

It is also a little odd that the species should have been mistaken for *S. flava*, for it has some rather distinct differences. Unlike the latter it never produces phyllodia, the flowers are dissimilar, and there are many differences in the pitcher. The latter are upright, seldom exceeding 26 inches (66 cm) in height, and they lack the bell-topped mouth of that species. The nectar roll, which tends to slope very slightly towards the front, lacks almost entirely the frontal 'spout' we see in *S. flava*. Other differences are evident in the hood. Here the column is shorter and wider, and its margins are not reflexed. Nor is the lid reflexed towards its edges, but is on the contrary concave on its ventral (lower) side, and overhangs the mouth at a lower angle, being sometimes almost horizontal. Pale green when young, the pitchers later acquire a yellowish-green hue in a sunny position, becoming longitudinally lined with straight red veins which continue into the hood. The whole pitcher may later become reddish, while in some forms the interior of the hood becomes a brilliant deep red contrasting with the green below. p. 51

The flower is easily distinguished from that of any other species, for the palest yellow to creamy-white colour of the petals is unique, and while in *S. flava* they are strap-shaped, in *S. alata* they are of oval form.

THE SWEET TRUMPET *Sarracenia rubra* This, the smallest of all the upright-pitchered *Sarracenias* in its typical form, was discovered by Walter, who describes it in his *Flora Caroliniana* of 1788. It is a rather variable plant, and there is debate as to whether the more extreme variants should be considered as subspecies, varieties or simply forms. In addition to the typical type (itself very variable), some botanists now recognize one, two, or even three subspecies. While the author advances no views on this matter it can be said that these plants are consistent in maintaining their distinguishing characteristics even when grown away from their native environments, and for convenience we describe them separately under their subspecific names.

Sarracenia rubra ssp. *rubra* is the typical form. It occurs on the eastern coastal plain in Georgia and South Carolina, and in the southern part of

Sarracenia rubra ssp. *rubra* RIGHT, and BELOW natural size, showing a hover-fly sipping from the nectar roll.

the creature drowns. It is in fact believed that this process is hastened by a wetting agent secreted by the glands into the water which denies the animal the buoyancy it could generally expect to retain.

On the evidence of its exceptionally wide geographical range and of the frequency of its occurrence within that area, it is clear that this is the most successful of all *Sarracenias*, yet it has often been remarked that its trap is much less efficient than those of other species. This belief must surely have arisen from the observation of cultivated plants under glass. These may catch no flies unless water is kept in the pitchers, and even then the number trapped may be small. In contrast, those kept out of doors will catch many more, and the pitchers of these plants in my collection are often a third filled with carcases before they die. Though these plants almost invariably have some rainwater in their pitchers, they seem to both attract and catch the greatest number of insects in bright sunlight immediately following rain, and at such times struggling flies are found in many of the pitchers. The reason for this seems far from clear; nectar secretion is not necessarily heavier at such a time, and the efficiency of the trap does not appear to be influenced by whether the trap is still wet with rain or dry. Likewise, pitchers of the Northern Pitcher Plant in plants naturalized in Ireland catch very considerable quantities of flies, and it may not be coincidental that this is an area of very high rainfall.

The part played in digestion by enzymes secreted by the plant itself seems to be minimal in this species; it is certainly much less than in any other in the genus, and it depends largely upon bacterial activity for the process. While this might be seen as a retrogressive step if it occurred in other *Sarracenia* species, the water provides accommodation for a vast multitude of bacteria, so that decay is both fast and efficient.

THE NORTHERN PITCHER PLANT *Sarracenia purpurea* ssp. *purpurea* When compared with the rather limited distribution ranges of other *Sarracenias*, that of this subspecies is truly enormous. At its south-eastern boundary in New Jersey it meets the northernmost boundary of the southern subspecies, *S. purpurea* ssp. *venosa*. Here typical forms of both subspecies are found, as well as intergrading types and hybrids. From this point the boundary stretches eastwards some thousand miles, then following an irregular north-westerly line it crosses the Canadian border, continuing to within one hundred miles or so of the Great Slave Lake in the Northwest Territory. Here it is able to survive bitter winters, with the January mean temperature as low as $-4°$F ($-20°$C), and it is undoubtedly its remarkable adaptability to varying extremes of temperature which has made it such a successful colonizer. From the New Jersey coast its eastern boundary follows the seaboard northwards to mid-Labrador.

The leaves of the Northern Pitcher Plant differ from those of the southern subspecies in the following ways. They are noticeably more narrow in proportion to their length, and tend to become longer in the mature plant. The upper pitcher is less bulbous, and the slim lower part is longer in proportion, which gives a rather different effect when observed in the field, for a large rosette may call to mind a cartwheel, of which the lower parts of the leaves are the spokes. The hood is smaller, and differs in that it does not undulate from side to side along the edges, and its lobes, unlike those in the Southern Pitcher Plant, cannot be readily drawn together with the hand so that they meet. Another difference by which it may usually be readily identified is that the exterior surface of the tube is very smooth to the touch, while in the southern subspecies it is rough. Differences in the flower do not provide a reliable means of indentification, for in some plants the flowers appear identical in both, but it can be said that the petals in the northern subspecies are as a general rule of a darker and rather brighter red, that the flower is usually very slightly smaller, and that its stem is a little narrower.

It was this subspecies which Clusius illustrated in 1601 (see page 26), but despite its wide distribution it was not till 1840 that Rafinesque recognized its distinction from the southern plant. He considered that the differences between the two justified giving each the status of its own specific rank, and named the northern type *Sarozina gibbosa* and the southern *Sarozina venosa*, an opinion which seems to have met with little support at the time. In 1933 these differences were recognized by Dr Edgar T. Wherry, but, noting that the two types intergrade, he considered them as subspecies of the one species. In naming them he used specific names taken from the subspecific names of Rafinesque. Thus the Northern Pitcher became *S. purpurea* ssp. *gibbosa*, but as this was the original plant to have been discovered and named *S. purpurea*, in 1972 he renamed it *S. purpurea* ssp. *purpurea*.

Though found normally in very acid bogs, acidity does not seem an essential requirement of the plant, but rather a common feature of the boggy and extremely impoverished conditions of the ground in which it lives, for it also occurs in alkaline marl bogs around the Great Lakes region. These have one thing in common with the acid bog: they are deficient in plant foods. The marl bog plant tends to be rather smaller, developing a greater number of pitchers to the rosette, and these tend to be rather more highly coloured than in the typical plant. Some say that these peculiarities are stable, and that they are maintained in cultivated plants, in which case the use of the varietal name, var. *riplicola*, would seem justified.

Attempts have been made to naturalize it in Europe, some of which have been successful. In a manuscript journal dating from some time in the latter part of the eighteenth century Thomas Collinson referred to *Sarracenias* flowering in the greatest profusion he ever saw in wet rocky ground at the Duke of Atholl's estate at Dunkeld in Scotland.

Taking into account conditions of climate and environment we can deduce with fair certainty that it was this plant to which he referred. Early this century it was also introduced into the Bernese Jura of western Switzerland where it is now firmly established in several bogs. In 1906 Benjamin St George Lefroy introduced plants to various bogs in Roscommon and Westmeath in Ireland. In some of these the plants have prospered and are now to be found in vast quantities. In 1930 Mr J. G. D. Lamb introduced three of the Westmeath plants to a bog in County Offaly. These soon seeded themselves over the area, where there are now countless numbers. Fortunately none of these bogs is easy to find, and to protect the colonies from the threat of depredatory collectors it is best to preserve the secrecy of the locations.*

An interesting mutant form, *S. purpurea* ssp. *purpurea* f. *heterophylla*, is sometimes found in nature. This has yellow-green pitchers which often shade to pure yellow around the edges of the hood, and the flowers are yellow. The peculiarity is caused by the absence of the red pigment anthocyanin in the entire plant. Such plants are of rare occurrence; they may appear in small numbers in the company of the typical plant, but occasionally they become dominant.

The Pale Pitcher Plant *Sarracenia alata*. In some forms the inner part of the hood is partly or wholly coloured red—hence the name 'Redthroat'.

THE SOUTHERN PITCHER PLANT *Sarracenia purpurea* ssp. *venosa* Despite the enormously wide distribution of the northern subspecies, it is undoubtedly the Southern Pitcher Plant which is the better known plant nowadays. There seems no obvious reason for this, unless it is due to its being the marginally more easily cultivated of the two. Its range commences from a point north of New Orleans eastward through the south of Mississippi, Alabama, the extreme north-east of Florida and south-east Georgia. There is an interruption in central Georgia, and the range then continues from the north-east of that state up to southern New Jersey, where it meets the southernmost limit of the northern subspecies. Here, in addition to typical plants of both subspecies, intergrading types and hybrids between the two occur.

It may be easily identified from the northern subspecies by the fact that the pitchers lack the external smoothness of ssp. *purpurea*. They are definitely rough to the touch, due to many microscopic white hairs, largely lacking in the other plant. The young pitchers, and the green areas in the older ones are also of a rather paler green. A major difference is in the form of the pitchers, which are shorter and broader, the bulbous part of the upper tube being so inflated as to be bell-like, while the mouth is proportionately wider. There is also a thicker nectar roll, which in transverse section is commonly twice the diameter, and it often projects noticeably outwards at the front to form a pouting lip. This is especially conspicuous when, as is often the case in summer, it is visibly wet with nectar. The hood is larger and, unlike the northern subspecies, it undulates towards the edges. Its network of coloured veins is often of a rather brighter crimson-red, in eye-catching contrast

*A stand of quite recent origin exists in northern England, but it would be unwise to divulge its whereabouts for the same reason. A few small plants and seed of Irish descent were introduced around 1960, since which time the proliferation has been astounding.

LEFT A wasp seconds away from losing its foothold on *Sarracenia* x *mitchelliana*. This natural hybrid between *S. leucophylla* and *S. purpurea* ssp. *venosa* occurs commonly where the two species grow near one another.

to the pale green interspaces, and these are somewhat bolder. Often, though by no means always, the flowers are somewhat different, tending to be from pale to middle pink rather than red, though red forms do occur, and the stems are usually stouter.

An account of the naming of the two subspecies is given in the previous entry, and we need only say that this plant retains as its subspecific name that given it by Dr Wherry in 1933. The plant is somewhat variable, though no anthocyanin-free form has been found. One Mississippi plant in the author's collection has an exceptionally well-developed nectar roll, which becomes deep ruby-red, while the whole pitcher becomes so suffused with red that the green is entirely obscured.

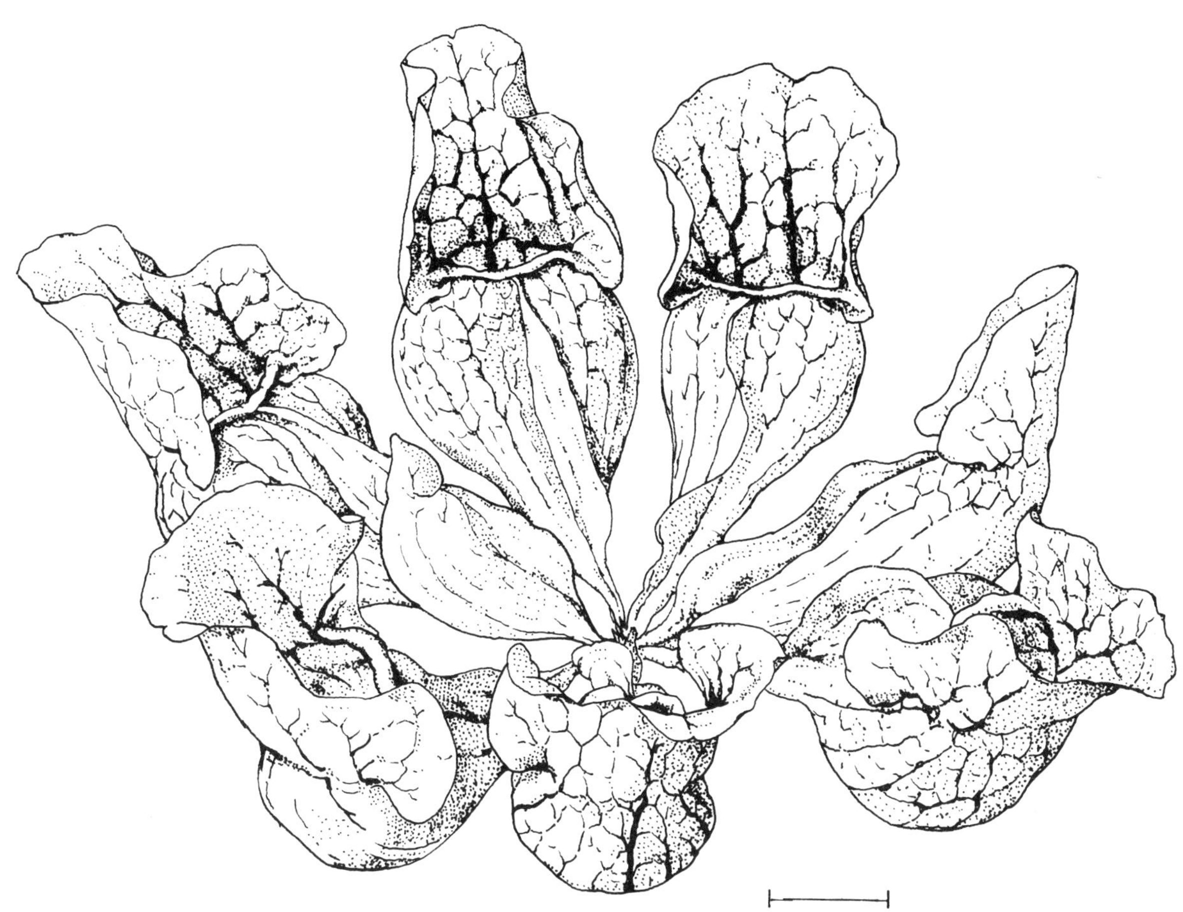

Sarracenia purpurea ssp. *venosa*

low, wet, sandy plains, subject to flooding by the acid water of nearby swamps, and it is evident that these are the conditions generally favoured. However, Schnell records the occurrence of extra large plants which grow together with the giant Hooded Pitchers peculiar to that place on the extraordinary floating sphagnum prairies of the Okefenokee Swamp.[7]

The tapering pitchers are usually rather small. They curl slightly backwards along their length and are surmounted by a rounded wing. Generally measuring between 4 and 8 inches (10–20 cm) in the mature plants, they sometimes reach a length of 12 inches (30·5 cm). Like the Huntsman's Cups (see page 46) they are decumbent, forming cartwheel-like rosettes; but in other respects they are all quite dissimilar, and in fact this plant is markedly distinct in general appearance from other *Sarracenias*. In place of the flap or hood of other species the top of the pitcher forms an inflated bulbous head terminating in a pointed, beak-like structure. The strong resemblance of this object to a parrot's beak accounts for both its Latin and English names. In the angle between the head and tube of the pitcher is the small rounded entrance or mouth. The form alone of the pitcher, while both strange and fascinating, is perhaps hardly beautiful; but recompense for any such shortcoming is to some degree made in the gay red and white variegation of its upper parts, and in its fine deep red flowers, rather similar to those of the White Trumpet, though proportionally smaller, and which possess a distinctly sweet fragrance.

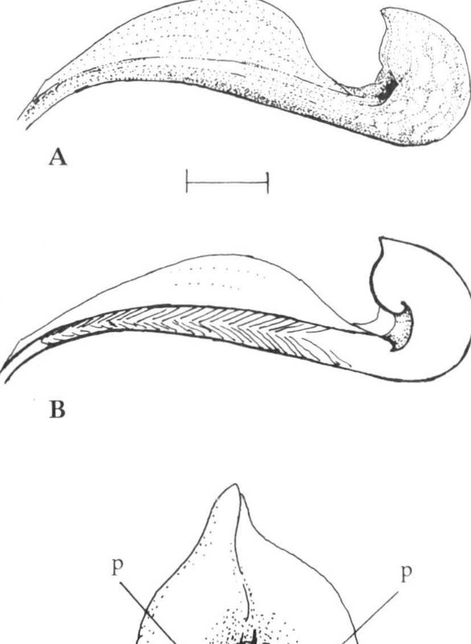

Sarracenia psittacina A: side view of pitcher. B: section to show the entrance tube and the no-return arrangement of hairs in the pitcher tube. C: cross section of tube to show the hairs within and the pathways (p) either side of the wing leading to the entrance tube and the brightly lit interior.

Further examination of the pitcher shows that the bulbous head has in fact evolved from the original hood. The beak marks the termination of the hood, while the seam, which runs centrally from the beak down to the top of the entrance, represents the joining of the two opposite lobes of the hood. Of equal interest is the short entrance tube extending into the pitcher from the mouth, which plays an important part in the working of the trap. This is formed partly from the frontal reaches of these same lobes which are enlarged and bent inwards,[9] but also partly from what once formed the nectar roll and the immediately adjoining wall, as can be easily seen from a simple dissection of the pitcher at this point. The wing arises from very near the base of the pitcher, broadening till it becomes relatively wide half-way, then gradually narrowing till it rejoins the tube just short of the mouth, where it is converted into a rib which runs the full length of the floor of the entrance tube. The central part of the ventral side of the pitcher is flattened or slightly concave, so as to form a path either side of the wing which leads directly into the mouth of the pitcher.

From a point approximately half-way along, the upper part of the pitcher is liberally mottled with white areolae or windows. These are rather more angular and straight-sided in form than in the Hooded Pitcher, from which they also differ in covering all sides of the pitcher including the head. In plants growing in shady conditions the areas between the areolae may remain predominantly green, the veins becoming tinged with red to some degree, but in sunnier places they turn from green through bronze to dark red, forming a network of mullions in vivid contrast to the white fenestration. As in the Hooded Pitcher, these windows play a prominent part in the working of the trap.

In a species with a trap of such different appearance and function to others of its genus it is perhaps not surprising that the internal zonations vary somewhat. The interior of the hood, here forming the ceiling and sides of the 'head', is Zone 1. As in other species, this is scattered with nectar glands, but the downward-pointing hairs appear to serve no particularly useful function and have become few and weak. Zone 2, which surrounds the pitcher in other species, is here found only in part of the nectar tube, while Zone 3, normally smooth and glandular though still retaining the digestive glands, is hairy, as in Zone 4. The down-pointing hairs of Zones 3 and 4 are, as will be seen later, proportionally much larger than in other species, their function also being rather different.

The fact that this plant favours places subject to flooding is significant, and it has been found that such periodic inundations are considerably to the plant's advantage. Such water contains numerous tiny aquatic animals, which the plant is uniquely adapted to trap. Indeed the volume of the catch made in times of flood often greatly exceeds the volume of land animals it can catch in the normally much longer periods when it is not flooded. Certainly the trap mechanism seems better suited for the capture of aquatic animals than it is for small crawling animals. No other carnivorous plants appear to possess this dual ability for trapping both aquatic and land-based life, and it is certainly true that no other pitcher plant is capable of catching water creatures. It is especially successful in trapping the smaller crustaceans such as *Daphnia* (the Water Flea), *Cyclops* and the Ostracods, and it may be that the trap has some special fascination for these animals.

LEFT *Sarracenia psittacina* actual size. RIGHT The translucent windows or areolae are conspicuous, as is the prominent wing guiding prey towards the entrance tube.

The Trumpet Pitchers: Sarracenia

Many crawling insects are undoubtedly attracted by the scent of nectar, but a proportion must encounter by mere chance the prostrate pitcher in the path of their wanderings, when they may then become attracted by its nectar, or by following one of the two paths run the risk of becoming accidental victims. The wing and the two paths provide convenient routes to increased nectar supplies, and both lead straight into the heavily nectared entrance tube. From these positions the way ahead will seem completely clear, for, as in the Hooded Pitcher, bright light comes from the windows on the opposite side of the pitcher. Such a clear path must seem unobstructed even for non-nectar feeders. A large number of insects reaching these points will enter the pitcher as a result of the same ruse we saw employed in the windowed Hooded Pitcher, but in the Parrot Pitcher escape is even more difficult, if not almost impossible, for the top part of the pitcher is a perfect lobster pot. As the insect makes for the apparent exit of the windows it finds itself barred; there is no indication that the narrow tube through which it entered provides an exit. Naturally it makes further escape attempts at other windows, and in searching it is encouraged to walk further down the tube, for this fenestration continues for some distance within. Indeed, windows are found well past the beginning of the region of long, perilous downpointing hairs which line the remainder of its interior, and which the insect is thus persuaded to enter. It may easily bend these hairs downwards, when they will part allowing a clear passage down the tube (see below), but pressed upwards they remain intercrossed, allowing no upward progress. Collectively, these hairs thus form a perfect valve which only allows advance in one direction, and the victim is thus conducted as far into the interior of the pitcher as possible, where it is firmly held by the same hairs. Thus, despite the horizontal lie of the pitcher tube and the consequent lack of gravitational assistance, the victims tend to accumulate in a solid mass from the pitcher bottom upwards. This is important, for this not only brings them to the place of most efficient digestion, but it ensures that maximum use is made of the available space.

LEFT *Sarracenia psittacina*. Within the pitcher tube the hairs make only downward progress possible for the struggling victim.

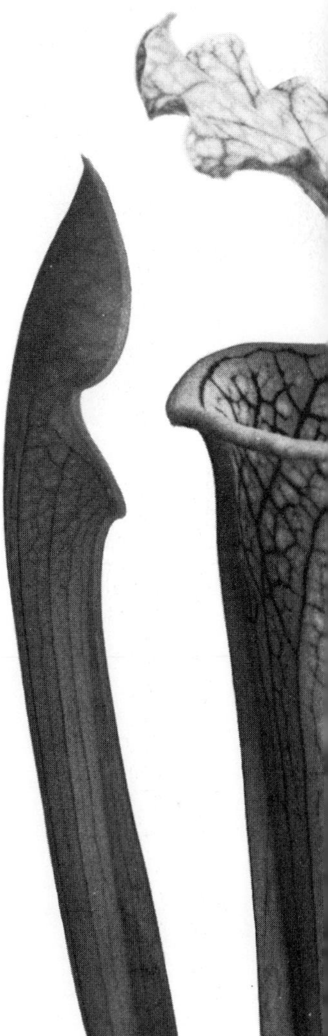

The hybrid *Sarracenia* x *mooreana*

Sarracenia: The Natural Hybrids

We have already seen that the *Sarracenia* flower is constructed to ensure pollination from other flowers. When it comes to fertilization, the species are all unusual in showing no apparent discrimination as to whether the pollen is of its own species or another within the same genus. Thus, should fertile pollen find its way from *S. flava* to *S. purpurea* before pollen from the same species, the likelihood that hybrid seed will result is high. As a result, natural hybrids are not at all uncommon in nature. Where two or three species grow in the same savannah one might, indeed, wonder why hybrids are not of even more frequent occurrence than they actually are. There are several factors which prevent this. In the first place, the peak of flowering time tends to differ between the species, so that the stigma in the flower of one species is unlikely to be receptive at the same time as the pollen is ripe in that of another. For hybridization to be possible, therefore, one or both blooms must be slightly out of season. Secondly, the species tend to differ in their preferred habitats, and this often rather isolates them from one another. Thus *S. purpurea* may be found in almost aquatic conditions in blankets of sphagnum where *S. flava* cannot grow. The latter species is usually found in more elevated and better-drained bog, into which the former will hardly penetrate. D. E. Schnell points to additional isolation factors concerning the pollinating insects: many insects remain faithful to the flowers of one species, while some are able to negotiate the flowers of some but not of others.[7]

When hybrids occur in most other genera, they are almost always sexually sterile, and cannot produce fertile seed. Here again *Sarracenia* breaks from the general rule and produces fertile hybrids. Where one such hybrid forms a suitable clump, several flowers may be produced, and the chances of self-fertilization occurring between these are good. Of the resulting seedlings, some will take after their parents in appearance, but others will show tendencies towards the likeness of one or other of the original two species which were their grandparents. On the other hand, where such a hybrid produces only one flower it cannot normally be self-fertilized. If this is pollinated at all the overwhelming likelihood is that it will be by one of the species in its hybrid make-up, for, due to the isolation factors previously outlined, it is not probable that the pollen of a third species will be available.

Sarracenia: The Natural Hybrids

Such back-crossing can result in endless degrees of gradation between the two species, so that it is neither possible to guess the order of their lineage when encountering such plants in the field, nor to distinguish them from the variant offspring of a self-fertilized interspecies hybrid.

In *Sarracenia* any hybrid between species is halfway in character between its parents, a characteristic which is very rarely found in other genera. Thus, a yellow and an indian-red flower crossed in this genus is

RIGHT *Sarracenia* x *formosa*
BELOW *Sarracenia* x *swaniana*

ABOVE *Sarracenia* x *wrigleyana*. LEFT *Sarracenia* x *catesbaei*. BELOW *Sarracenia* x *mooreana*, with a fly approaching the danger area.

likely to produce an orange-buff flower just as if mixed on an artist's pallette. A tall narrow pitcher crossed with a wide squat one results in a semi-erect, rather wide pitcher of middle height. This is also usually true when a hybrid is crossed with another hybrid or with a species. In producing hybrids artificially, this fact is extremely useful, for this predictability enables one to 'read in the dark' to some degree and plan in advance the plant one wishes to create. The possibilities open in this

Sarracenia x *courtii*

field seem endless, though strictly beyond the scope of this chapter, and I have therefore included further information on hand-pollination in the Appendix (page 228).

Due to this phenomenon, it is not surprising that early botanists tended to mistake interspecific hybrids for species, and named them in Latin accordingly. This seems to have become a habit, and names were later given to known hybrids both naturally occurring and of horticultural origin. This is now considered botanically inadmissible, but it is so much more easy to say '*Sarracenia mooreana*' than the cumbersome, but botanically correct, '*Sarracenia leucophylla* by *Sarracenia flava*', that the existing names will no doubt continue in use.

Though the eight recognized species can produce twenty-eight interspecific hybrids, this does not happen in nature, for to bring this about the geographic ranges of all must overlap, which does not happen in all cases. While some natural hybrids can be bizarre in form and inefficient in catching prey, rather more are attractive plants with efficient traps. *S.* x *excellens* (*S. leucophylla* x *S. minor*) is beautiful both in its pitcher and in its bright red flower, while the *S.* x *mooreana* referred to earlier produces elegant pitchers and large, fine pale-orange flowers. Perhaps the best known, most frequently occurring and far-ranging is the wide-pitchered *S.* x *catesbaei* (*S. flava* x *S. purpurea*) in which the older pitchers become richly red-veined, often turning crimson as they age. The following is a guide to the nomenclature of both natural and raised interspecific hybrids. Those occurring in the wild are marked (W).

Interspecies cross	Latin name
S. flava x *S. oreophila*	—
x *S. purpurea*	*S.* x *catesbaei* (W)
x *S. leucophylla*	*S.* x *mooreana* (W)
x *S. alata*	—(W)
x *S. rubra*	*S.* x *popei* (W)
x *S. minor*	*S.* x *harperi* (W)
x *S. psittacina*	— (W)
S. oreophila x *S. purpurea*	—
x *S. leucophylla*	—
x *S. alata*	—
x *S. rubra*	—
x *S. minor*	—
x *S. psittacina*	—
S. purpurea x *S. leucophylla*	*S.* x *mitchelliana* (W)
x *S. alata*	*S.* x *exornata* (W)
x *S. rubra*	*S.* x *chelsonii* (W)
x *S. minor*	*S.* x *swaniana* (W)
x *S. psittacina*	*S.* x *courtii* (W)
S. leucophylla x *S. alata*	*S.* x *areolata* (W)
x *S. rubra*	*S.* x *readii* (=x *farnhamii*) (W)
x *S. minor*	*S.* x *excellens* (W) (= x *cantabridgiensis*) (W)
x *S. psittacina*	*S.* x *wrigleyana* (W)
S. alata x *S. rubra*	*S.* x *ahlesii* (W)
x *S. minor*	—
x *S. psittacina*	— (W)
S. rubra x *S. minor*	*S.* x *rehderi* (W)
x *S. psittacina*	*S.* x *gilpini* (W)
S. minor x *S. psittacina*	*S.* x *formosa* (W)

Trumpet pitcher *Sarracenia* x *excellens*. A naturally occurring hybrid between *S. leucophylla* and *S. minor*, this can be one of the most attractive and richly variegated of pitcher plants. Its flowers are bright red.

The Cobra Lily: Darlingtonia

Darlingtonia californica (darling-tone-eea). Fam. Sarraceniaceae

p. 189

Though closely related to *Sarracenia*, the pitcher of the Cobra Lily is of rather different appearance from any in that genus, and is of more sophisticated construction. To even the most insensitive observer, the first glimpse of this plant must surely be an experience never to be forgotten. Complete with an expanded hood and forked tongue, the pitcher resembles nothing so much as a yellow-green cobra poised to strike. So great is the similarity that it seems strange indeed that this is a case of pure accident of design rather than of intentional mimicry; the unvarying local name wherever it occurs is as obvious as it is apt. The plant was discovered near Mt Shasta, California, in 1841 by J. D. Brackenridge, a botanist who accompanied Captain Wilkes on a government expedition from Oregon to San Francisco. It was described and named by John Torrey in 1853 after his friend Dr William Darlington.

There is only one species in the genus. Its range embraces the greater part of the Pacific coast in Oregon to a distance inland of about 130 miles (209 km), crossing the north California border and extending south-eastwards in a narrow tongue for some 250 miles (400 km). It generally occurs in mountains, commonly growing in sphagnum and peat bogs through which water is constantly seeping, and sometimes in wet ground to an elevation of some 8,500 feet (2,592 metres). It has therefore sometimes been regarded as essentially a mountain plant, although the presence of flowering colonies a few feet above the sea level here and there along the Oregon coast shows that elevation is not one of the critical factors in its habitat. Of far greater importance is a cool root run, for it has been observed that where the ground temperature is too high, the roots cannot survive, and the spring water emerging in the lower stations of the plant must be sufficiently cold to maintain this essential requirement, even though the air temperature may become hot.

The Cobra Lily rears its menacing head to lure insects by sight and smell into its pitcher trap. The spiral wing twists up to the mouth, partly hidden behind the fishtail nectary. Light shining through the windows over the back of the dome gives insects a false promise of escape.

The trap

The pitchers arise in a terminal rosette from a rhizome. In seedlings and on growing shoots they are decumbent (lying on the ground but with the apex or tip turning upwards) to semi-decumbent, but in the mature plant they are generally erect or nearly so. Their stature varies, surprisingly, in each plant and indeed in the individual rosette. They may reach 30 inches (75 cm) in height but a few on the same plant may not exceed 4 inches (10 cm). The tube widens gradually upwards, bending at its summit where it is inflated to form the dome-like hood. Centrally placed immediately below this structure is the downward-facing elliptic mouth. The wing ascending the tube is very similar to that in the erect-pitchered *Sarracenias* but of more regular breadth. It leads directly to the innermost corner of the mouth where it terminates. From the opposite outermost corner of the mouth hangs the forked tongue-like structure called the 'fishtail', from its general appearance. In a sunny position this assumes a brilliant red and green variegation, in vivid contrast to the yellowish-green to gold of the hood. Between its two corners the margins of the mouth are rolled inwards to form a substantial nectar roll. The upper part of the primitive leaf, which is seen as the lid-like hood in *Sarracenia*, is represented in *Darlingtonia* by the domed hood which terminates in the fishtail device, the latter representing the apex of the leaf. A most striking feature of the pitcher tube is that it is twisted along its length by one complete half turn, and this is made very evident by the spiralling of the wing. Individual plants in which the twist is clockwise or anticlockwise may be found, the latter seeming to predominate. This ensures that the mouth and fishtail appendage of each pitcher is outwardly displayed, which undoubtedly enhances the chances of attracting prey.

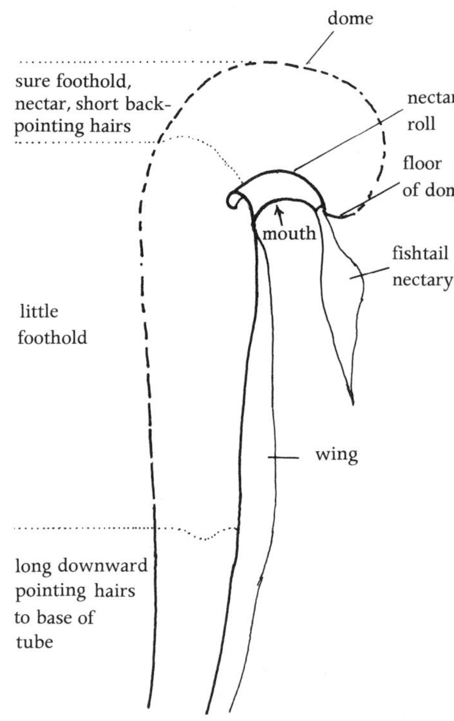

Darlingtonia: trap structure.

The roof of the dome is heavily spotted with windows or areolae. Though rather similar to those in the Hooded Pitcher, these are actually glass-like in their almost complete transparency, and, like the glass windows of houses, when seen from without they appear dark.

The entire exterior of the pitcher is scattered with small nectar glands. These are more numerous on the wing, and especially so on the fishtail, a main attractant to prey. They are at their most abundant on the nectar roll. Within the pitcher interior there are many on the floor beneath the nectar roll, and they also occur, though scattered, on the forward-facing and central area of the walls and ceiling of the dome, where they are intermingled with stiff pointed hairs which are directed backwards towards the tube. No glands of any kind are found in the rear part of the dome and in the adjoining uppermost part of the tube. This region is smooth, offering little foothold to insects. The remainder of the tube is clothed with long, thin, down-pointing hairs, which lack the stiffness of those in the front of the dome. This zone is also glandless, and, as one might expect, no digestive enzymes appear to be secreted by *Darlingtonia*, but water exudes from the walls, and may be found at the bottom of the newly opened pitcher.

Insects are persuaded to enter the pitcher by various routes. The brightly coloured fishtail appendage provides a popular landing and feeding ground, and in ascending it they enter directly through the mouth to the richly baited nectar roll. Others will alight on the hood and during their foraging will discover the same abundant supply. While some will land on the tube and be attracted to the same goal by the increasing supplies, and often with the guidance of the wing, the latter also provides the main path favoured by ants in their ascent from the ground to the nectar roll.

Once they have reached the nectar roll, the insects are already within the confines of the pitcher. Always restless, they may wander into the dome itself, or step over the roll on to the nectared floor surrounding it, which also provides an ideal standing ground for larger insects to feed from the roll. Those pacing the dome are already approaching dangerous ground, but insects choosing to remain on the floor or mouth are safe, so long as they remain there. When, however, they decide to depart, the most obvious exit appears to be the ceiling above, which, with its window-like areolae, appears open to the sky. They may fly directly against it and, in their efforts to escape, encounter the smooth surface at the rear where, losing their footing, they will slither into the depths of the pitcher. Others will crawl into the dome, and so find their way to the perilous zone and a similar fate. The sharp backward-pointing hairs on the ceiling undoubtedly encourage the smaller insects to walk in their direction. On falling to the bottom of the tube, the victims encounter the water. Their bodies and wings soaked, and a slippery surface above with down-pointing hairs poised against them, the chances of escape at this level are remote if not impossible.

Due to the apparent total absence of enzyme secretion in the pitcher, the bodies of the victims must be broken down in the water entirely by bacterial action. A nutritive solution is thus formed which is gradually absorbed by the pitcher. Water is thus important in the digestive process, and it has been found that it increases in volume as insects or other nitrogenous foods are added to the contents of the pitcher.

The graceful flowers appear in spring. They are nodding and are borne on tall stems which are clothed with several pinkish lance-shaped bracts. The five pale green sepals are tongue-shaped, pointed, and are rather larger than the petals. The five petals are predominantly crimson due to heavy veining, but there is a suggestion of yellowish-green between. When the sepals open the petals are at first drawn closely together to form a pointed hazelnut-shaped corolla. A most curious feature visible at this stage is the five circular holes towards the point of this structure, formed by the abutment of semi-circular indentations on the edges of each petal; they allow the only access to pollinating insects. As the flower ages the tips of the petals open a little and become free as far as these entrances. At petal fall the ovary is exposed to view. This is large, and of bell-like form. Centrally borne on the base of this bell is the star-shaped five-armed stigma. Seed matures rather rapidly, some ten weeks after fertilization. It is club-shaped, pale brown and hairy.

Darlingtonia flower. A: towards petal-fall the tips of the petals often open a little. B: section to show the flower parts.

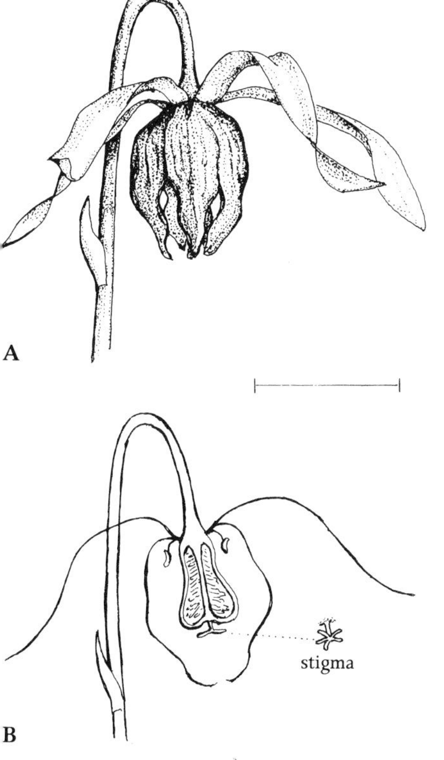

3 The Tropical Pitcher Plant: *Nepenthes*

Nepenthes (nep-en-theez). Fam. Nepenthaceae
This is the famous 'Pitcher Plant' known to most of us, if only from illustrations in encyclopedias. To human eyes it is certainly one of the most extraordinary of plants, for the handsome hanging pitchers, which appear to drip forth on long stems from the end of leaves, are of remarkable and most unleaf-like structure, and it is not surprising that the uninformed almost invariably confuse them with flowers.

First found by Europeans in Madagascar in the mid-seventeenth century, over sixty species have been discovered since then, some very recently. These are widely distributed in the tropics of the Old World, from Assam in the north through Malaysia and south-east Asia to Queensland in the south. They are also found in Ceylon, and Madagascar is their westernmost territory. It was not until the second half of the nineteenth century that they achieved popularity as cultivated plants in the great stovehouses of Europe and America.

The plants are typically climbers of damp humid jungles, where they may climb above 50 feet (15 metres). However they may quite often be found in rather drier, more open places, where they are non-climbers or scramble amongst low scrub or herbage. The thick vines attach themselves to supporting vegetation by means of tendrils emanating from the tips of the long flat leaves. These twine themselves around (usually in a single turn only) any stems or other supports they may touch, but the ends of the tendrils stand clear and it is from these that the pitchers may develop.

The trap

These are generally produced in the summer, but it does not follow that every leaf will develop one. Indeed, plants may be found entirely devoid of pitchers, though this is generally attributable to a cause, such as lack of light or, particularly in cultivation, low humidity. The first sign of pitcher formation is a noticeable swelling at the end of the tendril of a recently formed leaf. This grows fairly rapidly, the tendril hanging down due to its increased weight. As the rudimentary pitcher develops it becomes upright due to the bending of the adjoining part of the tendril.

As the flat 'bud' approaches maturity it is suddenly inflated with air.

A mature *Nepenthes* pitcher. In the background on the left can be seen the first stage in the development of such a pitcher—little more than a swelling at the end of the tendril. Also in the background, on the right, is an embryo pitcher in the halfway stage of development. The kink in the tendril will develop into a short spiral, to give the plant a hold on neighbouring vegetation. The specimen illustrated is *Nepenthes* x *williamsii*.

LEFT *Nepenthes* x *formosa* trap, representing a typical *Nepenthes* upper pitcher. Note that the tendril is attached to the pitcher at the back, not at the front as in lower pitchers. The spiral in the tendril is absent in lower pitchers. RIGHT Structure of a typical *Nepenthes* upper pitcher (A) and lower pitcher (B), and detail of the pitcher rim showing the position of the nectar glands between the teeth (C).

Nepenthes

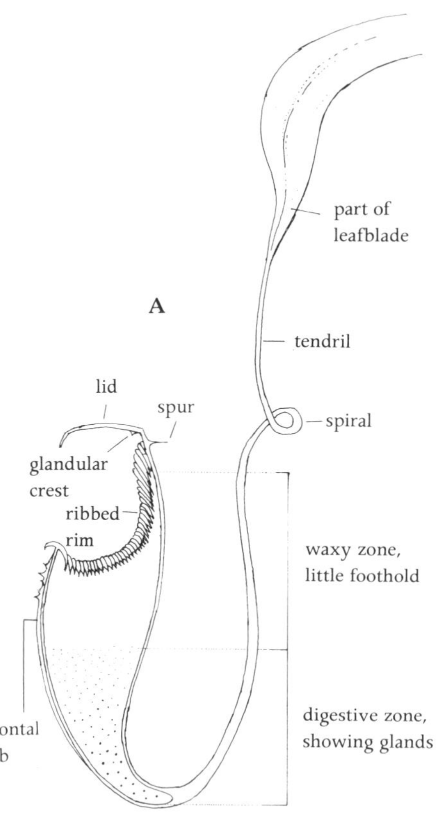

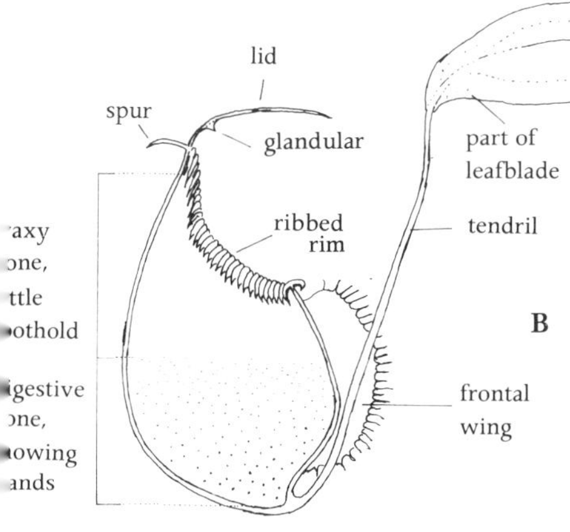

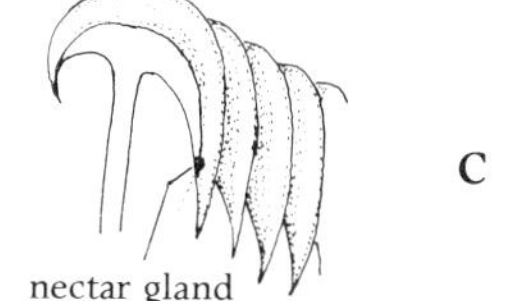

At about this time the first splashes of colour appear in the variegated species, but the lid remains firmly closed. In time, the variegation increases in intensity and area, and after a few days the lid opens. At this stage the bottom of the pitcher is already charged with fluid, secreted after inflation. Even though the pitcher is now operative, its walls are still weak, but they harden during the next few days, and a week or ten days after opening the pitcher may be said to be fully mature. There is a popular belief, shared by some of the early botanists, that the lid closes upon its prey. This is not the case; indeed, were it so, this would considerably limit the catching capacity of the trap. The lid's function is twofold. Firstly, it is a seductive device; flying insects are attracted by the nectar-secreting glands which liberally cover its inner surface, and to these it offers a convenient foothold. In many plants the lid is brilliantly coloured, which no doubt further advertises its nectar. Secondly, in most species it forms a rain-protecting canopy over the mouth. This is important in areas of high rainfall, since without it the pitcher would soon fill up with water and overflow, thus losing nutritious liquid and its effectiveness as a trap.

The pitcher mouth has a rim or collar which is hard, glossy and rounded. This is corrugated very regularly with parallel ribs which are often made conspicuous by contrasting red, green and occasionally white variegation. Each rib terminates within the pitcher in a sharp downward-pointing tooth, and within the angles between these are single nectar-secreting glands.

The body of the pitcher varies in shape very much according to species, and there is often slight variation in shape from pitcher to pitcher on a single plant. Indeed, some species carry pitchers of two or even three different forms at different levels on the same plant. The typical form is more or less cylindrical with a rounded base, the lower half being often slightly bulbous. In the lower pitchers of most species the two 'wings' which run parallel on the front of the pitcher are a conspicuous feature. When highly developed they are fringed with hairs or bristle-like teeth. In the upper pitchers the wings are usually replaced by ridges which may continue from their point of emergence just below the rim down as far as the base of the pitcher where they merge with the tendril.

The interior of the pitcher below the rim is usually divided into two zones. That immediately within is a glaucous waxy area, usually extending about one third the way down. The remainder consists of a smooth, glassy, glandular surface which is pitted with numerous microscopic glands. This is the digestive zone, and the glands not only secrete the digestive fluid found in the bottom of the pitcher, but also absorb the foods resulting from the digestive process.

The food supply provided by the nectar glands is soon discovered by ants, and it attracts many winged insects also. Many of the latter will alight on the pitcher itself, or upon the nectar-rich lid, but there is a general tendency to pace about in search of a more abundant supply, and sooner or later many insects will find their way to the drops of nectar between the downpointing teeth of the inner rim. The narrow rim itself offers a precarious foothold to many insects, especially those of the housefly type, but that this is not universally the case was noticed by Dr F. E. Lloyd and Professor Kupper in observing the behaviour of visiting ants.[9] These persistently visited the lid and rim. While on the lid they were known to be in perfect safety, but up to that time it was supposed that the rim provided no foothold. This proved not to be the case, for they could be seen running backwards and forwards along it rapidly without risk, the smooth shiny surface offering an ideal hold for their footpads. However, it was noted that a very large quantity of ants had been caught by the pitcher. They were in no danger unless they wandered on to the wax zone immediately beneath the rim. Here the loose wax easily broke away, clogging their footpads, and usually resulting in their loss of foothold, thus accounting for the thousands of bodies discovered in one pitcher. Foraging animals tend to move constantly, and this is certainly true of insects imbibing the nectar, for even those which apparently find a convenient foothold on the rim are inclined to pace about till their feet are partly or wholly on the wax zone. Besides, the spacious wax zone must appear to offer a rather more convenient platform, and as far as large insects are concerned, the rim provides too limited a space to accommodate all their feet, and these are bound to seek a foothold at least partly on the wax surface. Once on it, the odds are that they will lose their grip, and that they will fall into the abyss below.

Once caught in this way the animal may struggle in the fluid until it drowns. This does not take long, for the liquid has a marked capacity for soaking and is indeed thought to contain a wetting agent. Such activity immediately excites the digestive glands which then secrete acid and enzymes heavily, the fluid showing a marked increase in acidity within a few hours. Others, especially small insects, will swim to the sides and may succeed in scaling the wall for some distance, but in doing so, they again excite the glands on which they walk into secreting more juice, and the minority that manage to retrace their steps as far as the wax zone are unable to scale it.

Digestion in *Nepenthes* is efficient and rapid. In nature a medium-sized fly may be completely digested in two days leaving only the hard chitinous skeleton, while a midge-like fly is digested within hours, though in cultivated plants the process takes longer. Bacteria, though present in all but newly opened pitchers, play at most only a very secondary role. If tested for acidity, the fluid of an unopened or newly opened pitcher is generally neutral in reaction, but shortly after suitable food is added a gradual acidification occurs. This is important, for the enzymes, just as in the human stomach, cannot act without the presence of an acid. During the process of digestion, this acidity

4 The West Australian Pitcher Plant

Cephalotus

Cephalotus (sef-al-o-tus). Fam. Cephalotaceae

Cephalotus follicularis is a plant of curious appearance even amongst pitcher plants, and is the only species both in its genus and in its family. It has a very restricted range, being found only in St Georges Sound on the extreme south-west coast of Australia. Here it mainly inhabits peaty swamps, amongst wet sand in a mainly coastal area, approximately two hundred and fifty miles long by little more than fifty miles broad at its widest point. It was first recorded and possibly discovered during the French expedition to southern Australia led by d'Entrecasteau in 1792. The naturalist was La Billardière, who published a description of the plant in 1806. Plants were introduced to Kew in 1823, where it was successful, flowering some years later.

The roots are thick and branching. The leaves are of two types: the non-carnivorous foliage leaves and the pitcher leaves, and they are borne in a rosette. This surmounts a taproot in the seedling, after which they are borne as terminations of root branches. The foliage leaves have been probably incorrectly termed autumn or winter leaves. While it is true that they may grow during the winter months under artificial greenhouse conditions it seems that this does not occur in nature. Mr Stephen Clemesha, who has observed the plant in its natural habitat, states that they are produced in spring, and this is also normally true of my own cultivated plants. They are oval, pointed, flat, and of a bright glossy green. The petiole also is flat, rather short, and tends to be hidden by the other leaves in the rosette. These leaves last for approximately a year, withering as the fresh crop is produced.

Production of these spring leaves normally ceases towards the end of the season. At about this time, the embryo pitchers become evident as tiny hairy hedgehog-like forms around the centre of the rosette. As they grow, so the stalk-like petioles lengthen until they are borne beyond the perimeter of the rosette. At this stage they are approaching full size, and when the petiole ceases to grow the pitcher comes to rest permanently on the ground, its front away from the rosette. It lies at an oblique angle, its base forward. A few days afterwards the lid opens. In shade the pitcher remains green, but in sunny positions it acquires a vivid deep crimson-red coloration. It may exceed 2 inches (5 cm) in length in nature, but is more commonly around $1\frac{1}{4}$ inches (3 cm) long.

The squat and bristly pitchers of *Cephalotus follicularis*. In the centre can be seen the pale green non-carnivorous spring leaves.

The flowers are about $\frac{1}{8}$ inch (3 mm) across and inconspicuous. There are no petals, and the six sepals are greenish-white. They are borne in a short panicle at the end of a tall slender stalk which often exceeds 24 inches (61 cm) in height; surprisingly tall for so small a plant.

The trap

The singular form of the pitcher has been compared with a moccasin slipper, its sideless heel having been curved over to form the lid. The belly is short and tubby, curving forwards towards the base, the outline of its body in profile being suggestive of the lower half of a bean. The mouth has a well developed rim, which is strongly ribbed in a manner reminiscent of *Nepenthes*. There are three pronounced ridges which run down the front of the tube from immediately under the rim to the base, and the lid is cockle-shaped and set at an angle. The leafstalk is attached to the rear of the tube just below the union of the lid, whereas in all other pitcher plants it joins the bottom of the pitcher. Indeed, in general construction, the pitcher does differ considerably from those of other genera. We see it also in the three ridges previously referred to and in the origin of the lid, which does not represent the terminal part of the leaf as in other pitcher plants, but has been shown to have been derived from extensions of the leaf base.

The primary function of the three ridges would appear to be to guide insects towards the mouth. Of these, the central ridge is most highly developed. T-shaped in cross-section, it consists of a keel which expands along its margin to form a wide, slightly concave raised pavement at right angles to its blade, and this is edged on either side with stiff hairs. The other two ridges are laterally placed and first descend obliquely backwards, curving forwards in the lower part where they proceed to the base of the pitcher. Keel-like and edged with hairs, these do possess the rudiments of the T-forming cross-member, but this feature is so undeveloped as to be scarcely noticeable.

The oval mouth has a distinctive rim which is prominently corrugated with glossy ribs. These curve over and into the pitcher where each terminates in a sharp downwardly directed spine. The cockle-shaped lid overhangs the mouth, preventing the entry of rain. From about its middle, pleat-like ridges develop and proceed to the margin, sometimes branching as they go. In the furrows between these a limited number of long and rather narrow, colourless, translucent 'windows' are found. These areolae are similar to those in *Sarracenia minor* and *Darlingtonia*, but their function may be different. Nectar glands are scattered over the entire surface of the tube excluding the rim, and they are also found on the external and internal surfaces of the lid.

A curious and somewhat unusual feature of the internal structure of the trap is the thick wide collar below the rim which overhangs the well. This is normally pure white, smooth and shining, and is covered

Cephalotus. A: side view of a pitcher, and B: section

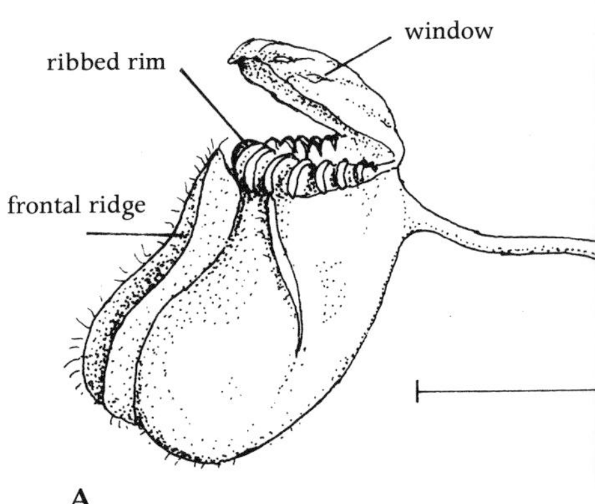

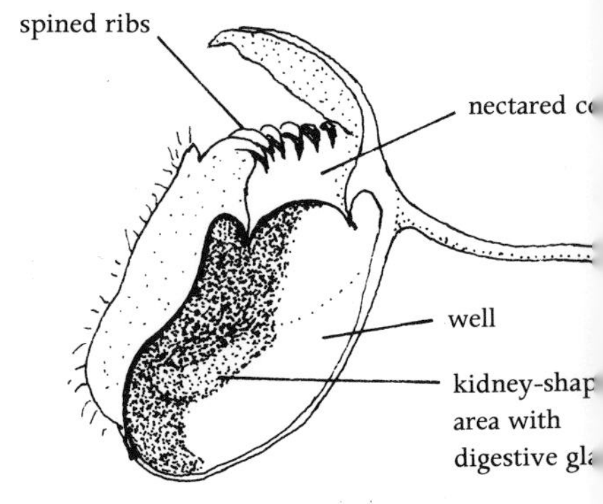

with many nectar glands. Its lower edge in section terminates in a point, for the bottom surface of the collar slopes downward from the pitcher wall. A device is thus formed which is practically impossible to negotiate for insects attempting to escape from the well. The sides of the well are also glossily surfaced. In its upper part are numerous digestive glands, but these are entirely lacking towards the bottom. About halfway down on each side is a slightly raised, long kidney-shaped area of an intense magenta-black. On both of these the digestive glands are especially numerous and some are much larger than elsewhere in the pitcher. The coloration tends to spread from these areas, suffusing less intensely much of the frontal surface of the well. A certain quantity of fluid secreted by the pitcher is to be found in all but the oldest pitchers.

The small but exquisitely moulded and intricately constructed trap is undoubtedly most efficient. Particularly alluring to ants, which it catches in large numbers, it attracts many flying insects also. These are clearly attracted primarily by the nectar glands which are scattered over the entire external surface, but its prey is by no means restricted to nectar feeders, as the evidence of the pitcher contents will often show, for many seem to be the victims of chance, and, finding the pitcher in their path, are likely to be guided to the mouth by one of the three ridges.

Similarly, nectar feeders will tend to walk towards the mouth sooner or later, whether they are on the body or lid of the pitcher. Here they are likely to sense the presence of the abundant source of food on the nectar collar within. On this the slippery foothold offered is so hazardous that they may lose their footing more or less at once, falling into the watery fluid below. Should they retain their hold, they will have difficulty in making their exit via the rim in face of the opposition of the sharp downpointing teeth, and in their efforts to do so they run further risk of falling. Insects which have dropped into the well are unlikely to escape from the fluid due to its clogging effect on their bodies and the slippery nature of the surrounding walls. They will drown and be digested, in part by the enzyme protease which is present in the fluid. Should an insect manage to extricate itself from the liquid it will find access to the collar made difficult if not impossible by the structure of its lower edge described above, and in the unlikely event of its succeeding, it will be confronted with the hazards in that zone already described. What part do the windows play? F. E. Lloyd considered that 'they are to insects apparently open spaces, and the insects are thus tempted to escape from them, to rebound to the depths of the pitcher.' However, Rica Erickson feels that 'the light that falls through the panes is mirrored in the fluid below', and such shining spots may attract the insects. It seems feasible that they may play a double role, and that there may be truth in each theory.

5 *Genlisea*

Genlisea (jen-liss-eea). Fam. Lentibulariaceae

This is a curious genus, bearing traps of complex structure quite unlike those in any other genus. It belongs to the same family as the Butterworts and Bladderworts. It is indeed a close cousin of the latter, bearing very similar flowers, but it employs a totally different technique in catching its prey: that of the lobster pot or, as Darwin put it, like 'the eel trap, though more complex'.

It is an aquatic, and, except for the flowers which are borne above the water, the whole plant is submerged. Sixteen species occur in tropical regions in South America, the West Indies, Africa and Madagascar. All are small plants, the length of the trapping leaf varying between 1 and 6 inches (2·5 and 15 cm) according to species, the footstalk included. All are very variable, which has led to much

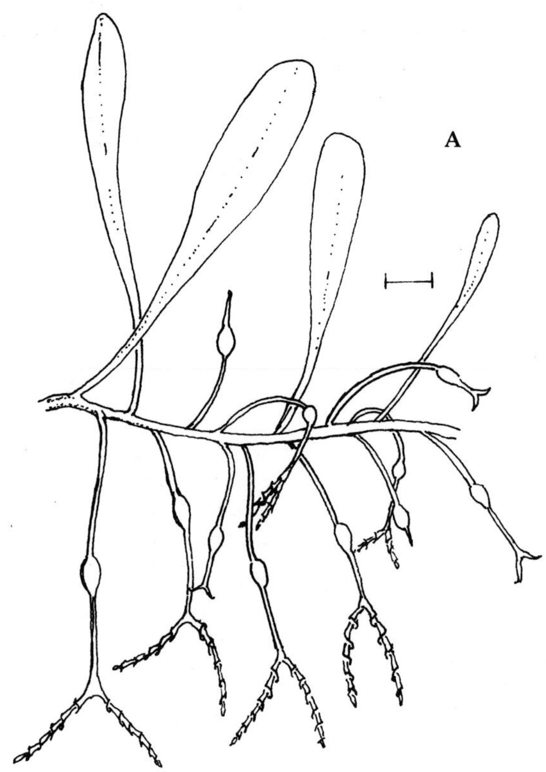

Genlisea. A: part of a typical plant showing the foliage and trap leaves.

confusion in nomenclature, and none appears to be at present in cultivation. It is therefore simpler here to deal with the genus as a whole rather than with individual species. The leaves are of two kinds: the foliage leaves which are either spoon-shaped or linear, and the trap leaves. Both arise in no particular order from a slender and occasionally branching rhizome (see A).

The trap

The strange form of the trap leaf is shown in B. It consists of a cylindrical footstalk (a), and a hollow bulb (b) from which issues a cylindrical neck (c). At the end of this is a slit-like mouth (d). The trap forks here into two branches, the mouth extending in a spiral for the length of each, for they are both twisted (e). The trap leaf also grows in a peculiar manner. The footstalk at first resembles a shoot, the end of which is pointed. This continues to lengthen, then just short of the tip the bulb is formed. The tip continues to grow, forming the neck, the end of which divides to form two wings, which then grow to become the spirally twisted branches.

The entrance at the end of the neck is shown in the diagrammatic cross-section C. It will be seen that the lip formed by the ventral side is rather shorter than the lip of the dorsal side opposite. Immediately within, on the walls of both sides, are tiny claw-like cells which, while allowing animals to enter, will deter their making exit. Beyond are transverse rows of long, sharp, inward-pointing hairs. These rows are continued at intervals to form lines of as many as fifty hairs (f), which in turn slightly overlap the hairs of the row below. These rows thus form cone-shaped valves which allow the inward progress of any animal, but exclude any possibility of its moving in the opposite direction.

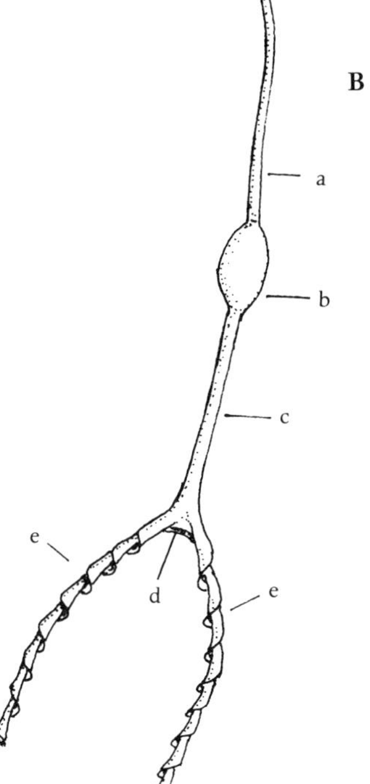

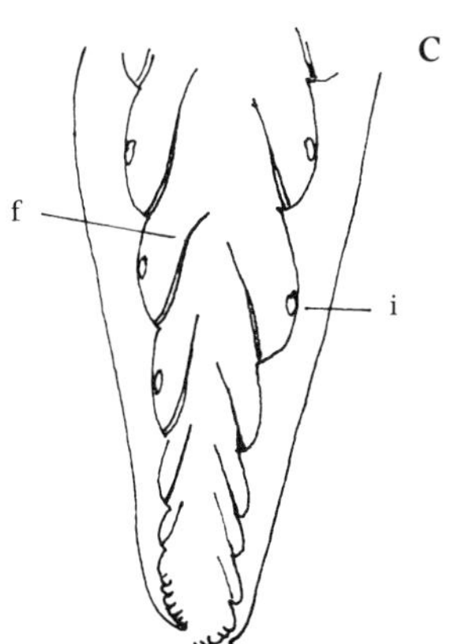

B: an enlarged trap leaf, and C: section through the entrance. For the indentification of the key letters, see accompanying text.

For as long as the animal is live and moving, therefore, it must ultimately reach the confines of the bulb, which may be seen as the trap's 'stomach' (D). Hence the victim will ultimately die, its soft parts being broken down into a liquid from which nutriment will be absorbed into the plant. On the walls here are many glands which are crowded mainly upon two ridges (h) which extend, one on the ventral and one on the dorsal side, for a third of the distance towards the neck of the bulb. These are thought to be both digestive and absorptive in function. In the neck and also in the branches, another rather smaller type of gland (i) is found just below the ridges which support the valve-hairs. The precise function of these is unknown, but it has been thought that they may secrete mucilage which, acting as a lubricant, could thus aid the progress of larger animals.

As the slit-like entrance continues from the mouth of the neck along both of the spiralled arms (E and F), the upper lip of the mouth becomes the outer one on the spiral, becoming reflexed outwards to form a sort of continuous funnel (g) which allows better access for prey. The inner and outer lips are wedged permanently apart by enlarged cushion-like cells which occur at intervals. The lips possess claw-like processes (see cross-section of branch G) followed by rows of downpointing hairs similar to those of the tube.

The advantage to the plant of the spiral growth has been variously interpreted, F. E. Lloyd's theory appearing the most logical. He pointed out that it results in the presentation to the prey of entrances to the interior, from whatever direction they may approach. It is not clear whether the trap has any particular power to attract its prey, however. The outer parts are scattered with stalkless (sessile) glands which secrete mucilage, but it is not known whether this is of an alluring nature. Undoubtedly, curiosity alone might account for the capture of the creatures, for once they move within the mouth return would be uncomfortable, and further within, impossible. The remarkable length of the mouth and its spiral arrangement in the arms must, in this case, considerably assist its chances.

Strangely, all the species of *Genlisea* appear to await introduction to cultivation, and adequate descriptions are not forthcoming from herbarium specimens.

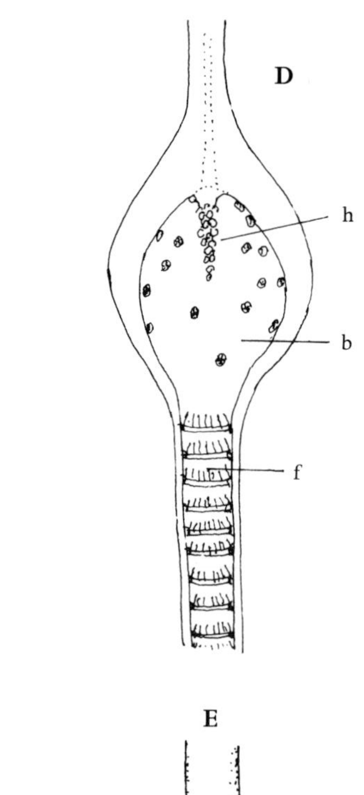

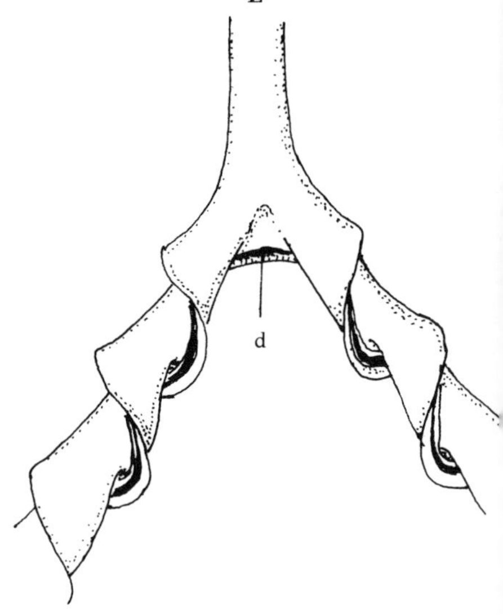

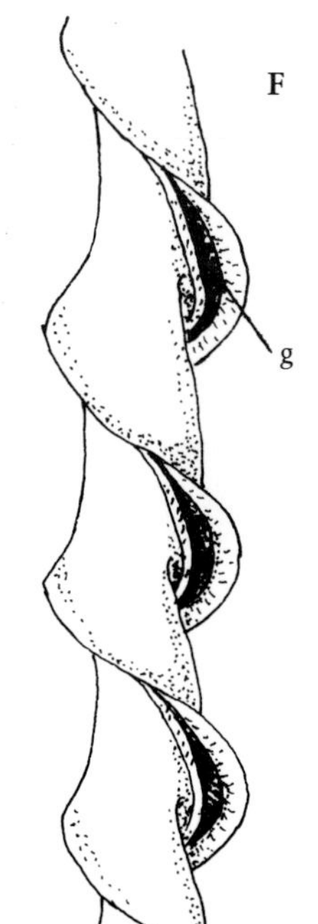

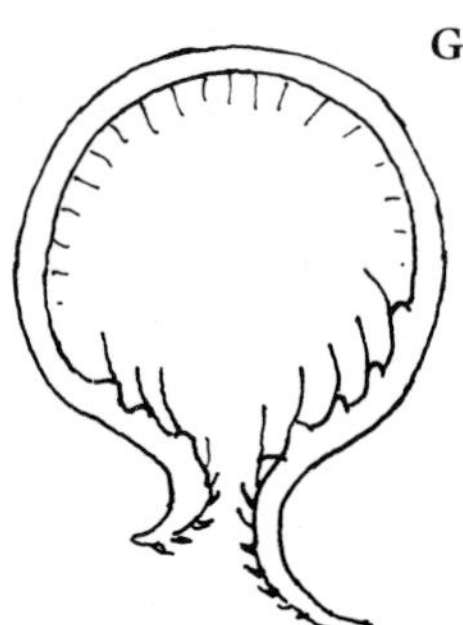

Genlisea. D: section through the bulb. E, F and G: position and structure of the trap entrance. For key identification, see accompanying text.

6 *The Passive Flypapers*

The plants in this group belong to two genera: *Byblis* and *Drosophyllum*. There is certain superficial resemblance between the two in their general appearance and in various features which they share in common. However, this is purely an accident in evolution, for they belong to quite separate families. Each plant secures its prey by means of a sticky mucilaginous substance secreted by numerous stalked glands. Both also possess other, sessile glands, which secrete enzymes around the victims' bodies and are digestive in function. In this way all but the chitinous husks and wings of the victims are broken down and dissolved into a fluid which may thus be readily assimilated by the plant.

These plants are described as 'passive' in the sense that they have not evolved that power of movement which we shall see in the sticky leaves of the Butterworts, and in the gland-tipped 'tentacles' and often in the leaves themselves of the Sundews. But it is very questionable whether such added sophistications would be of any real advantage to them at all, for both genera are so designed that they can efficiently catch and digest a truly remarkable number of insects.

The Rainbow Plant: Byblis

Byblis (by-bliss). Fam. Byblidaceae

This is an Australian genus of only two species. One, *B. gigantea*, is almost shrub-like in appearance, while the other, *B. liniflora*, is much smaller. Both are most attractive plants when seen in full growth, bedecked with soft violet or lilac flowers, their leaves and stems heavily set with glistening drops of mucilage. An allusion to this dewy appearance is found in the generic name. Byblis was the beautiful daughter of Miletus, who was the son of Apollo. She fell deeply in love with her twin brother, but her love was not returned, in fact he turned and fled. Shedding the tears of a broken heart, she was then mercifully turned into a fountain.

The leaves are narrow, tapering gradually to a point, which under a lens is distinctly knobbed. In cross-section they are more or less triangular. When mature they are held at an acute angle to the stem; the underside rather than the top surface of the leaf is therefore the most exposed, and provides the most obvious surface on which an insect in flight might land. Not surprisingly, then, it is the undersurface of the leaf which is used principally by the plant to detain its prey. This is heavily scattered with stalked, mucilage-secreting glands, but these are almost entirely lacking on the upper surface, where those that occur are of diminutive size.

In *Byblis* the stems, flower stalks and even the sepals are also thickly scattered with the glands, and in the sunshine the plants appear to shimmer with countless jewels. It is said that in their native habitat the drops tend to split up this light into all the colours of the spectrum, collectively causing rainbow effects, hence no doubt the common Australian name. This may well be so, but rather disappointingly my own plants have to date stubbornly refused to do this.

While the stalked retentive glands are large and very conspicuous, the digestive glands, though extremely numerous, are of microscopic size and quite invisible to the eye. They are arranged in single rows, and are sunk for protection in little furrows. They are to be found not only on both sides of the leaf, but also on the stems. In this *Byblis* is unique, for the digestive powers in all other sticky-leaved carnivorous plants are limited to the leaves. The identity of the digestive enzymes is not at present known.

Byblis is able to catch a surprisingly large number of insects on its leaves and stems and sometimes appears completely covered by them. Even those which alight on the top surface of the leaf, which is largely wanting in retentive glands, are liable to be caught by the sticky glands projecting sideways from the edges of the underside.

Byblis gigantea. Close-up of leafblades to show the stalked glands which hold the prey. Each leaf terminates in a distinct 'knob', as seen in the young leaf in the centre. BELOW Natural size.

The species

Byblis gigantea This species is confined to Western Australia, where it was first discovered by the botanist and collector James Drummond. From a point some fifty miles south of Perth it ranges some three hundred and seventy miles northwards. Favouring sandy, poor soils, it prefers moist rather than sodden conditions during its growing period. Growth commences annually with the winter rains, when shoots appear from the woody basal stem. These grow quickly, are erect and stout but wiry, reaching up to 2 feet (61 cm) in height before the land dries out during the hot dry summer. This yearly drought brings about the cessation of growth, the shoots die back, and the plant remains dormant till the onset of the next winter rains.

Despite its specific name, this plant is hardly gigantic; but it is much larger in its individual parts than the other species, *Byblis liniflora*. Though usually some 9 inches (23 cm) in length, the leaves can reach 12 inches (30 cm). Both these, and the stem from which they rise, are of a yellowish green.

observed for the first time that the leaf margins are capable of movement, and he was soon able to prove that the leaves both digest and absorb their victims.

There are two kinds of gland on the leaf surface. The primary function of the stalked sticky gland is to catch and detain prey, but it has recently been shown to also play a secondary but very minor role in digestion. It has a colourless, almost transparent stalk which is often somewhat bulbous a little above the base, but this narrows towards its top, which supports the gland proper. The latter is pill-shaped with a flat base, rounded sides and a shallowly domed top. The globule of mucilaginous fluid secreted by this gland is supported entirely by its sides and top. The other kind is stalkless, and is consequently referred to as the sessile gland. It secretes no mucilage, being always 'dry' unless in action. In shape it is similar to the stalked gland, but is a quarter the size, and is seated in a slight depression, only the summit of the dome being flush with the leaf surface. This makes it remarkably difficult to detect under magnification without the use of carefully contrived sidelighting. This tiny gland is much more numerous than the larger kind, and it is this which is primarily responsible for digesting the prey and for the absorption of the resulting nutrient fluid.

Trapping the prey

It is not yet satisfactorily established whether the leaves have any special means of attracting prey. They are not endowed with nectar glands, and though they do possess a slightly fungoid scent, whether or not this is itself alluring to insects remains an open question. They certainly catch a sufficiency for their needs, the victims consisting of midge-sized flies, winged aphids, springtails, tiny creeping insects and the like, which are often caught in great numbers. They seldom retain anything approaching the stature of a house fly, the small size of their victims being compensated for, no doubt, by their quantity.

The movements of an insect alighting on the leaf are immediately impeded by the sticky glands, its struggles only serving to bring itself in contact with others. Moreover, its presence soon stimulates them into exuding further mucilage and the victim is shortly overwhelmed and suffocated.

Digestion

This newly secreted fluid differs from the globules the glands normally support in being mildly acid. This is important, since the presence of acid is essential to the normal digestive process. The fluid also contains a few enzymes, but the main supply of these emerges from the sessile glands which are now excited into activity. They pour forth quantities of their secretion until the victim's body is engulfed in a pool of liquid. The combined action of acid and enzymes rapidly reduces and dissolves the soft parts of the insect, when the resulting nutritive fluid

Two Mexican butterworts: *Pinguicula mexicana* on the left, and *Pinguicula caudata* in the foreground.

Pinguicula caudata RIGHT is easy to grow as a houseplant. LEFT Large insects are not normally detained—this fortunate fly has reached the safe foothold of an unfurling leaf. BELOW Close-up to show stalked mucilage glands. On the left it may be possible to see the dark depressions which hold the sessile digestive glands. BELOW LEFT An entrapped fly on a curling leaf.

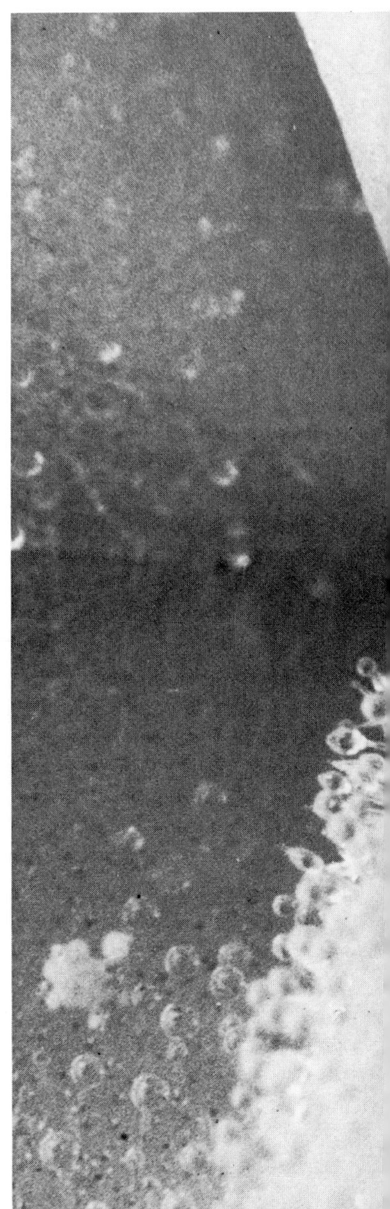

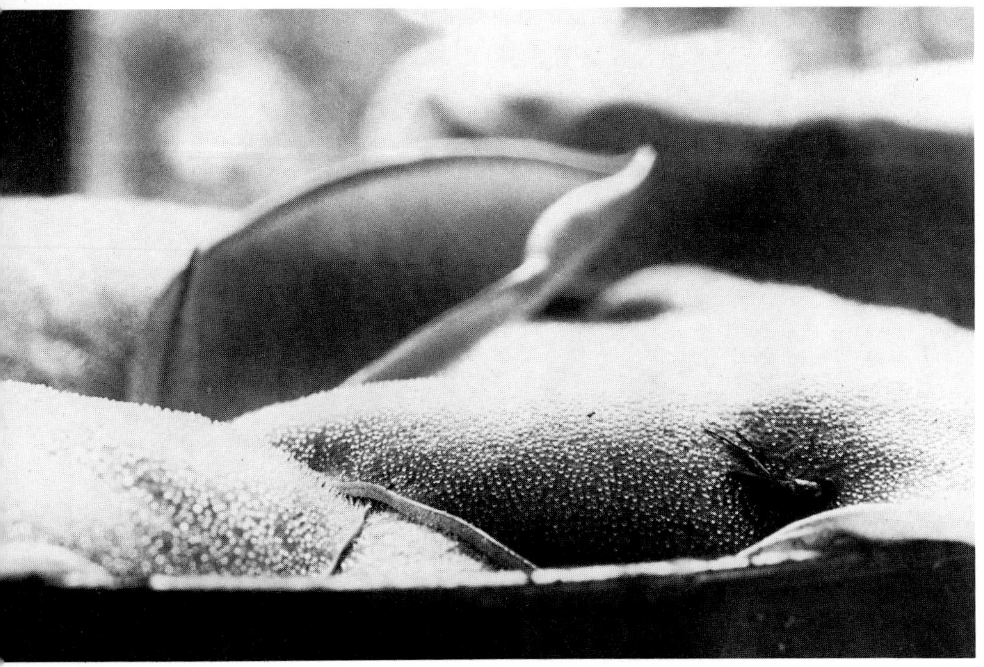

Pinguicula

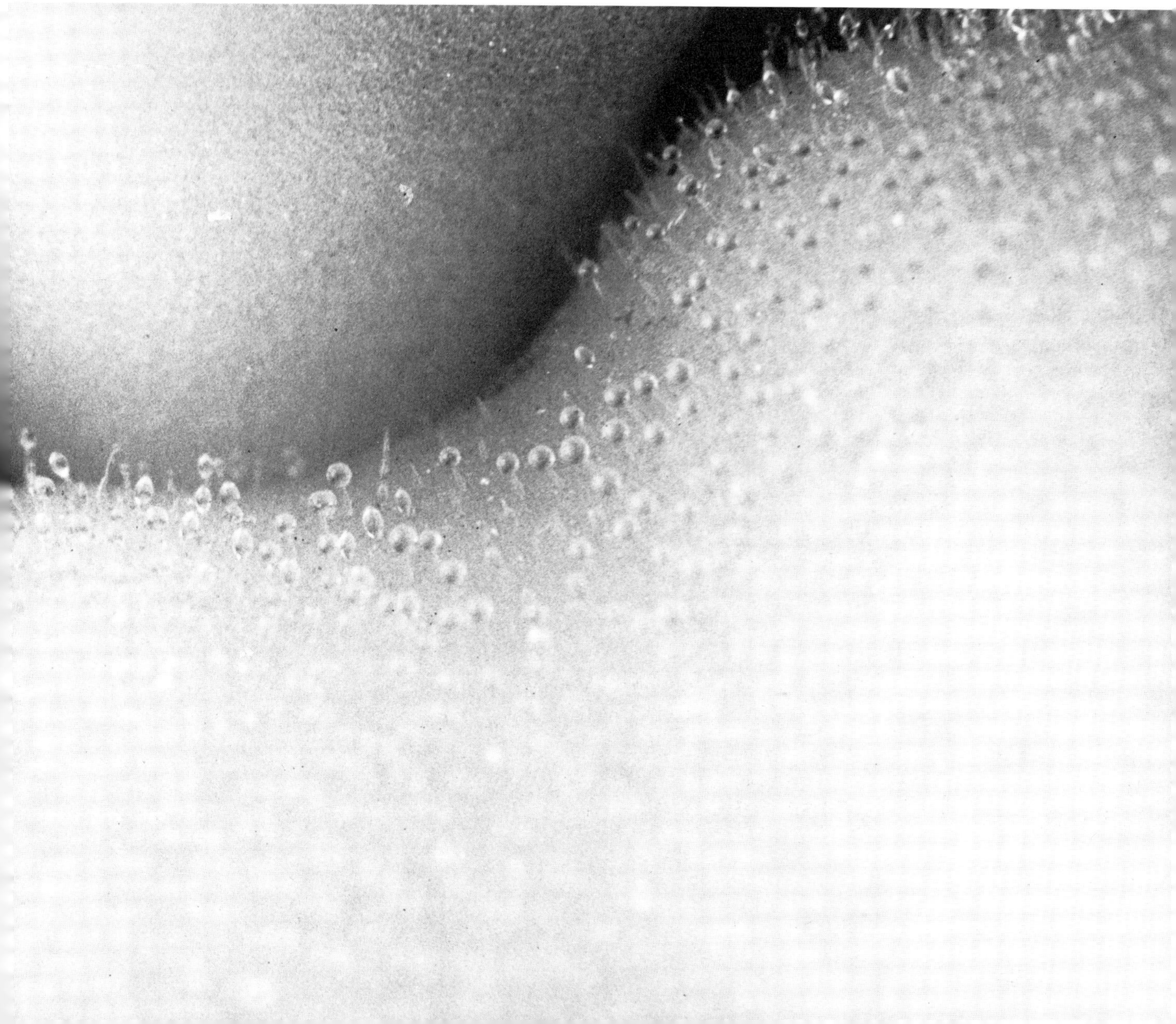

is absorbed into the plant's system by way of these same sessile glands. Known enzymes involved are ribonuclease, esterase, acid phosphatase, amylase and protease.

Bacterial activity appears to play little if any part in digestion. Indeed the secretion seems to contain a mild bacteriocide and there is little doubt that such activity would be harmful to the leaf, the surface of which is very delicate. If for example a rather larger insect than would naturally be caught is placed upon the central area of the blade, the digestive juices cannot penetrate sufficiently to bring about complete digestion of the uppermost part. Consequently bacterial activity sets in here, and spreads through the entire body of the victim to the leaf. This results in the death of the area of leaf immediately under and surrounding the victim, and often of a wider area, and it sometimes results in the death of the entire leaf.

Movement in the leafblade

In the vast majority of species the leaf is endowed with powers of movement. These are seen both in the capacity of the margins to roll over the bodies of victims within that area, and in that of the interior surface to become 'dished' under prey. Both processes are most obvious after larger prey have been overcome, and may not occur at all during the catching of smaller insects. The use, if any, to the plant of these movements has been much questioned. As the inflection of the margin is a slow process, seldom taking less than two days to complete, it can, contrary to a much repeated fallacy, play no part as an entrapment mechanism. Certainly, both movements bring about a speedier digestion: the dishing of the blade makes a vessel which retains a pond of the digestive juices in which much more of the victim's body is immersed than could otherwise be so, while the inflection of the margin over an insect exposes a far greater area of its body to direct contact with the glands. But can increased speed of digestion be of any real advantage to the plant, for if it were slower, would not the same quantity of resulting nutriment be ultimately absorbed into the plant's system? This is not necessarily the case, for there is always the possibility of loss before or during digestion, principally from rain which, if sufficiently long or heavy, will wash the nutritive fluid from the leaf's surface. It is therefore in the plant's interest that digestion is achieved as rapidly as possible, especially in places of high rainfall where many species occur. In species which frequent such areas (e.g. *Pinguicula vulgaris* and *P. grandiflora*) inflection of the permanently upturned or slightly rolled leaf edge is especially marked, as is its capacity to roll over victims. One useful function of these edges is to prevent insects' bodies being washed off the leafblade, while a second advantage of the inflection is to cover and thus protect the body from the rain. Indeed, without this safeguard the advantage of carnivory to the plant would be much less in these areas of frequent rainfall.

Species forming winter resting buds

In winter most of those species indigenous to temperate climates die down to a tight bud. This may be seen forming in the centre of the rosette in late summer and is called the winter resting bud or hibernaculum. It is entirely without roots in the majority of species and may therefore be shifted by water, frost action or snow, or by animal activity, all of which may be assisted by gravity. Where the buds fall upon inhospitable terrain there are undoubtedly some losses, but this is probably outweighed by the advantage to the species in assisting in its dispersal.

In addition most form gemmae. These are in effect tiny winter buds which, like hibernacula, are formed in late summer, but in the axils of the leaves. When the latter die back these are seen attached around the base of the hibernaculum. Some may break off due to the action of the elements which will distribute them, while many are scattered about the ground if the hibernaculum itself is displaced, but those that remain around the parent are later smothered by the expanding leaves of the parent plant in the following season. In some species the gemmae afford a means of propagation superior to that of seed in terms of increase in a single colony. *P. grandiflora*, for example, may produce as many as fifty.

In spring the hibernaculum opens slightly to allow the new leaves to emerge and at the same time a new set of roots descends into the ground. The process is identical in the gemma, except that the rosette thus formed is minute, but many of these will reach semi-maturity by the following autumn.

There are fourteen hibernaculum-forming species, of which I will describe three of rather wide distribution.

The Common Butterwort
Pinguicula vulgaris

THE COMMON BUTTERWORT *Pinguicula vulgaris* is of fairly widespread occurrence in Europe and Siberia, and also in the greater part of Canada, penetrating over the border into the United States in the Great Lakes area and in the highlands of the Pacific Coast as far south as north California. While essentially a plant of wet soils, it differs from most carnivorous plants in growing equally well in acid, neutral and alkaline conditions, and is especially common by mountain and moorland rills, on sunny banks where water is continuously seeping and on black peat. It is a handsome plant, the neat rosettes of narrow pale green leaves scarcely failing to attract attention, especially as they cling, like vegetable starfish, flat against the contours of wet rock faces—a familiar sight amongst the hills and mountains, where they may occur at altitudes of some 7,500 feet (2,290 metres). In such places too, its elegantly spurred 'violets' are seen to their best effect.

The leaves are oblong, blunt-ended, and about half as wide as long, but appear rather narrower at first sight due to their upturned edges. The summer rosette is between $1\frac{1}{2}$ and 6 inches (3·5–15·5 cm) in diameter. There are usually two or three stalks 2–5 inches (5–13 cm) tall. Each bears a violet flower with a white spot at the mouth. The corolla lobes are rather wide with rounded ends, the upper lobes being about half as long as the lower ones. The mouth is wider than high. The combined length of the tube and spur does not exceed $\frac{3}{4}$ inch (2 cm), the one merging rather gradually into the other.

Strangely diverse but mainly beneficial properties were attached to this plant in the past. In Elizabethan times it was supposed to protect cattle from the mischief of elf arrows, and humans from the influence of witches and faeries, while from the famous 1635 edition of Gerard's *Herbal* we learn that the husbandmen's wives of Yorkshire used to anoint the dugs of their kine with its 'fat and oilous juyce' whenever they were chapped, rifted, or 'bitten by any venomous worme', a practice which probably had its merits, and indeed alpine peasants were known to be still annointing the udders of their cattle in this way comparatively recently. The leaves were recommended in the late eighteenth century as an effective means of killing human lice. They were at one time much used in Scandinavian countries to curdle milk, and probably still are in Lapland. The milk may either be poured over them, or the mucilage of the leaf may be mixed in by smearing it on the container or sieve. A ropey substance forms which does not separate from the whey and which the Lapps call Tätmiölk. But despite its varied uses, this was not a popular herb with farmers, for it received the blame for causing the dreaded Liver Rot in sheep—a not unreasonable belief as it happened, for wherever the Butterwort occurred there, too, was found the Rot. It has since been discovered that the disorder is caused by the Liver Fluke, a curious animal which spends two parts of its complicated life history as a freeswimming organism in wet ground, another as a parasite of a small snail which is found there, and a fourth, if it is lucky—after it has attached itself to a blade of grass which must be swallowed by that animal—as a parasite of sheep.

Pinguicula grandiflora ssp. *rosea* differs from the type in having pale pink flowers and reddish rather than green winter resting buds.

Pinguicula grandiflora This is native to France, Switzerland, Spain and Ireland, and is known in Britain as the Irish Butterwort. In England it has long been naturalized in Cornwall. It occurs in an equal variety of habitats as *Pinguicula vulgaris*, tending rather more often to favour limestones. The leaves, too, are rather similar but more oval. The flowers, which are borne on 3–7 inch (7·5–18 cm) scapes are rich violet purple, with a white patch at the mouth. They are about 1 inch (2·5 cm) long and nearly as wide, and very showy. The usually interlocking lobes are wide, as is the mouth, and there is a long spur. Indeed, from the front the bloom bears a striking resemblance to a small Gloxinia. A very pale, almost white form occurs in County Clare in Ireland where it often grows with the typical form in limestone soil, while in Europe another a shade deeper in tone is found in the Jura mountains. A subspecies with pale pink flowers, *P. grandiflora* ssp. *rosea*, occurs only in the mountains near Grenoble in France.

pp. 105, 211

Pinguicula

THE ALPINE BUTTERWORT *Pinguicula alpina* occurs in most of the mountains of Europe and Asia. It ascends to some 5000 feet (1525 metres) above the tree line, descending to sea level in northern Scandinavia. It grows in various soils, and though often found in typical bog, it can grow in rather drier conditions than most species. The leaves tend to be rather pointed and more triangular than elliptical, seldom exceeding 1 inch (2·5 cm) in length. The scape may be 4 inches (10 cm) tall, the flowers white with an orange to yellow spot in the mouth, while the conical spur curves downward. The roots do not die away in winter in this species, so that the resting buds remain anchored to the ground during winter.

Once native to Scotland, where it occurred only in a bog on the Black Hole of Cromarty, it has long been extinct there, almost certainly due to the agency of man.

Pinguicula alpina growing to the left of a Birdseye Primrose (*Primula farinosa*), which favours similar conditions. Natural size.

Pinguicula lutea. The leaves can vary in length according to certain conditions. Here they are somewhat shorter than normal.

Species not forming winter resting buds

Of these there are two types: those which produce the same type of leaf throughout the year, and which are called the homophyllous growth type, and those which produce one type in the summer, termed the generative rosette, and another in the winter, the vegetative rosette. The latter are known as the heterophyllous growth type.

Homophyllous growth type

Pinguicula hirtiflora This species occurs in southern Italy and the eastern Mediterranean. The leaves are rather similar to those of *P. caudata* in general appearance, but are characteristically suffused with red in the marginal areas. They are also smaller, the entire rosette being usually about $4\frac{1}{2}$ inches (11·5 cm) in diameter. The flowers are about $\frac{5}{8}$ inch (1·5 cm) in diameter, and are borne on 3–5 inch (7·5–13 cm) scapes. They are mauve, the corolla being paler towards the wide throat. The lobes are mottled. Externally the throat is pale green, about $\frac{1}{4}$ inch (6 mm) long, while the spur is greenish white and up to $\frac{1}{2}$ inch (1·3 cm) in length.

Pinguicula

Pinguicula lutea This is one of six species which occur in the south-east United States. Its range extends from the extreme east of coastal Louisiana, eastwards through Florida and northwards to the southern corner of North Carolina. It favours open positions in damp rather than wet sandy soil. The leaves are pale yellowish green, oval-oblong, with their edges sharply enrolled. They form a rosette 3–6 inches (7·5–15·5 cm) in diameter. The scapes are about 4 inches (10 cm) high. The flower is unusual in being a rich chrome yellow, and is an inch or more in diameter. The hairs of the bearded palate are of a darker shade, and this structure projects from the corolla noticeably.

Pinguicula caerulea Occurring in the coastal plain of North and South Carolina and Georgia and in most of Florida, this is an attractive species in bloom. The leaves are of a duller pale green but of similar form to *P. lutea*, and form a rosette up to 4 inches (10 cm) in diameter. The flowers are borne on tall scapes up to 8 inches (20 cm) long and have a pale violet ground which is beautifully pencilled with darker violet veins. The mouth is rather wide and there is a projecting beard of greenish-cream.

Pinguicula lusitanica This tiny species occurs in North Africa, Spain, Portugal, France and Britain, where it is called the Pale Butterwort and is found in south-west England, west Scotland and Ireland. It is locally common in acid bogs, favouring wet naked peat surfaces on which it is often found at the side of moorland rills or at the base of tussocks in peaty seepages. The leaves are almost transparent, usually a very pale green and netted conspicuously with thin red veins, but in sunny places they acquire a pinkish hue. Up to $\frac{3}{4}$ inch (2 cm) long, their margins are almost completely rolled over to reveal even lighter undersides. This clearly protects much of their surface from rain, but there are possibly other advantages. They catch only very small, mainly crawling creatures.

The flowers are pale lilac pink, which is lightest at the front part of the corolla and on the spur. The corolla is of unusual form, being trumpet-shaped, the short lobes of both the upper and lower lips combining to form the flared bell, which is about $\frac{1}{5}$ inch (5 mm) in diameter. The entire flower including the spur is only $\frac{1}{4}$ inch (6 mm) long. The slender scapes are pale green to pinkish green.

The Pale Butterwort *Pinguicula lusitanica*. Though tiny, this is a pretty and free flowering species.

Heterophyllous growth type

pp. 108, 109

Pinguicula caudata This is a large and beautiful Mexican species. The summer leaves are thick and succulent, and are sometimes suffused with pink in sunny places. They are oval, often being as much as 4 inches long by $2\frac{1}{2}$ inches (10 by 6·5 cm) wide. In a single plant they are flat and ground-hugging, but a clump is soon formed when the leaves of adjoining rosettes will be drawn up against one another in the centre. The flowers are borne profusely for a long period in summer and again for a second period in the winter. The flower stems are a pale green, from 6 to 9 inches (15 to 23 cm) long. The flat-faced flowers are rather large, and may exceed 2 inches (5 cm) in length by almost as much in width. The lobes are almost rectangular with rounded corners, but the middle lobe of the lower lip is centrally indented at its end. They are carmine pink, becoming paler with age and with three rather deeper veins running down for a variable distance. Each has two carmine flecks at its base. The throat is narrow and white, while the slender spur is greenish white and up to 1¾ inches (4·5 cm) long. p. 106

In winter, the large summer leaves gradually die away, and are replaced by smaller ones, about half their size, which are more numerous and tightly applied one upon another. Those produced latterly are neither sticky nor carnivorous.

This species has been much cultivated in greenhouses for its beauty, and orchid growers have used it in the past to catch a small fly which lays its eggs amongst orchid seedlings. It was once sometimes known as *P. bakeriana*, and some authorities now consider it as a variety of *P. moranensis*.

Pinguicula mexicana This, like *P. caudata*, is now considered to be a variety of *P. moranensis*. However, due to their very different flowers it is convenient here to continue the error still general amongst gardeners of separating them. It, too, comes from Mexico, and has similar though slightly smaller rosettes of summer and winter foliage. The summer leaves are proportionately a little narrower than those of *P. caudata*, and may reach up to 3½ inches (9 cm) in length. However, the flowers, though violet-like, are otherwise dissimilar. These are borne on pinkish-green scapes 6 inches (15 cm) tall. They are smaller than in *P. caudata*, the face seldom exceeding a length of 1⅛ inch (2·8 cm). The petals are narrower, their ends often rounded, sometimes terminating in a slight point. They are of a very dark carmine pink, each netted with still darker veins, but there are no flecks at their bases. The throat is of a pinkish greeny-white, while the narrower spur is greenish pink and up to about 1½ inches (3·5 cm) long. p. 106

Pinguicula gypsicola This most unusual species was first discovered in Mexico in 1910 by Dr J. A. Purpus, Curator of the Darmstadt Botanic Garden. He found it growing on wet gypsum rocks in San Luis Potosi. The pale green summer leaves are up to 2½ inches (6·5 cm) long and differ from other species in that they are very narrow, seldom exceeding $\frac{1}{10}$ inch (2·5 mm) midway and gradually tapering to a blunt point. They arch upwards when young, the older leaves later becoming more spreading. The margins differ also from others in being reflexed backwards. The upper surface of the leaf is covered with mucilaginous

Pinguicula gypsicola. The spidery summer rosette is markedly different from that of any other known species. BELOW Natural size.

glands. The leaves catch very small flies, but are entirely devoid of the powers of movement common to other species. The purple flowers are rather narrow-petalled, are white-throated and long-spurred. They are some $\frac{3}{4}$ inch (2 cm) in diameter and are borne on stems up to $3\frac{1}{2}$ inches (9 cm) long.

In late autumn the summer leaves gradually die away while the winter rosette forms. This is a small flat radial rosette composed of numerous small succulent leaves which are minutely hairy. These do not secrete mucilage, and are non-carnivorous. It very much resembles that of a *Sempervivum*, and is capable of withstanding a period of drought. Indeed, it appears to have few if any roots, being anchored to the ground mainly by the dead ones from the previous season, but by late spring young roots are sent forth again, to be followed again by the sticky carnivorous leaves.

Pinguicula gypsicola. Two winter rosettes. The long outermost summer leaves are gradually dying away.

The Sundews: Drosera

Drosera (Dross-er-a). Fam. Droseraceae
In this genus the upper surface of the leafblade is thickly covered with tentacles. These are usually of a reddish colour, and each is crowned by a drop of clear colourless mucilage which glistens in the sunshine like dew. It is not unnatural that such a plant should attract the wonder of the earlier botanical writers, and it is interesting to note that one such author, Henry Lyte, the botanist squire of Lytes Cary Manor in Somerset, may have been the originator of its English name, for he has the following to say in his *New Herbal* of 1578:

> This herbe is of a very strange nature and marvelous: for although that the sonne do shine hoate, and a long time thereon, yet you shall finde it alwayes full of little droppes of water: and the hoater the sonne shineth upon this herbe, so muche the moystier it is, and the more bedewed, and for that cause it was called *Ros Solis* in Latine, which is to say in Englishe, the Dewe of the Sonne, or Sonnedewe.

It was not till the eighteenth century that the insect-trapping capacity of the leaves appears to have attracted much attention. Thus the English poet-scientist Erasmus Darwin concluded that the mucilage served to protect the foliage from insect attack,[11] a natural assumption in the absence of contrary evidence, while the American traveller-botanist William Bartram was able to observe that the insects were entrapped apparently deliberately, but seems unable to have explained the advantage to the plant.[12] But by the mid-nineteenth century its carnivorous nature was increasingly suspected, and when the grandson of that same Erasmus, Charles Darwin, completed his experiments on its leaves, final proof of their character was at last obtained. This he published in his book *Insectivorous Plants* of 1875.

The genus is a large one, at present comprising over ninety recognized species, to which several recent discoveries in Western Australia are likely to be added. Species occur in both hemispheres and in most countries and climates. Almost all are found in poor, generally acid soils, usually in bogs, but in Australia many species have evolved which are adapted to grow in much drier habitats, which may dry out seasonally or for considerable periods.

The species differ enormously in size and habit. The leafblade may

vary in length from as little as $\frac{1}{20}$ inch (1·5 mm) to over 2 feet (60 cm). It may be simple or much divided, and can be borne in a rosette at ground level, or singly on a tall or even climbing stem. The upper surface bears tentacles. The root may be either fibrous or fleshy, or the stem may shoot from a tuber.

The flowers are sometimes single, or there may be several or many to a stem. In one species they average $\frac{1}{10}$ inch (2·5 mm) in diameter, while in another they measure nearly 2 inches (5 cm) across. There are generally five petals which may be in almost any shade from white through pink, purple and red to orange and occasionally yellow, according to species, form or variety.

As a rule the longest tentacles are to be found around the leaf margin. These tentacles are generally only able to bend in one direction—towards the centre of the leaf—but they usually respond to stimuli with greater haste and move more speedily than do the inner tentacles (in *D. burmanii* they may move through 180° in less than a minute). They are thus particularly useful in preventing the escape of larger insects. These tentacles are held outwards, more or less in line with the plane of the leafblade, but they are slightly reflexed. From the margin of the leaf inwards the length of the tentacles gradually diminishes, while at the same time their angle of inclination steepens until in the central zone of the blade they are very short and entirely upright. Stimuli may be produced by irritation, as when a tentacle is lightly scratched, or by even a minute weight such as a tiny seed, or by the application of either a solid or liquid nutritive substance. If, however, tentacles are induced to close over a non-nutritive body, they will usually return to their original positions within twenty-four hours.

The tentacles consist of gland-tipped stalks of fairly complex structure. The glands themselves are egg-shaped, and usually develop a red coloration, especially when exposed to sunlight, even if the remainder of the tentacle remains green. They crown the stalks in an upright position, except in the case of the outer tentacles of some species (e.g. *D. rotundifolia*), where the tip of the stalk is then flattened into a little 'spoon' in the centre of which the gland stands.

These glands are quite unique amongst those of other sticky-leaved carnivorous plants in possessing three distinct and equally important functions. They not only secrete the mucilage which catches and overcomes the prey in the first instance, but they also secrete the enzymes (peroxidase, acid phosphatase, esterase and protease have been found) which, in association with a weak acid contained in the mucilage, dissolve all but the chitinous skeletons of their victims. Lastly, they absorb much of the resultant fluid into the plant's system. It is, however, more than probable that the latter task may be shared to a very small degree by microscopic hairs which are scattered on the leaf surfaces, and occur on the stems of the tentacles themselves.

The Round-Leaved Sundew *Drosera rotundifolia*

The Sundews: Drosera

The trap

Insects alighting on the central area of the leaf will be held, at least temporarily, by the viscid secretion of those glands on which they settle. Very large creatures may break free, but most will struggle, making contact with and thus activating neighbouring tentacles. By some as yet unestablished means signals are sent through the blade to activate further tentacles. The number being brought into action by this means depends much upon the resistance put up by, as well as the size of, the animal, and in this way sufficient are brought into use to thoroughly secure and overwhelm it.

Of course, not all insects are caught in the central zone of the leaf; rather the reverse in fact, for the outer glandular area is larger. But here digestion could never be as efficient due to the lesser number of available glands. However, this is a problem which the plant overcomes, for if an insect alights on this area the tentacles are soon seen to bend inwards, gradually conveying the creature to the central zone where it is secured, and where the glands are most numerous. The bending of the tentacles was found by A. Batalin to be due to a growth phenomenon, and was examined in more detail some twenty-five years later by H. D. Hooker.[13] To inflect, it begins to grow minutely in length from the base upwards. But the sides grow unequally, the outer more than the inner, so that the stalk is forced inwards. After digestion is complete, the process is repeated on the other side of the tentacle, which thus returns to its former position. As there is a limit to the total growth of the tentacle, the process of bending may only be repeated three times in one tentacle. Economy is therefore important. Thus a tiny midge alighting on an outer tentacle may be completely overpowered by the single drop of mucilage, and may be transported to the centre zone by this tentacle alone.

In many species a lesser or greater part of the leafblade itself may become tightly folded over the victim. This action does not show signs of starting till the insect is already overcome, and usually takes between twenty-four and forty-eight hours to complete; it therefore plays no part in the trapping of the victim, despite often-expressed views to the contrary. Its main advantage is clearly in the bringing of a greater part of the leaf, and therefore more glands, into contact with the insect. In this way more rapid and efficient digestion will be brought about, and it is not surprising that it occurs most frequently when larger victims are caught. It also plays a useful but secondary role in providing protection from rain, thus preventing the liquid products of digestion from being washed away before they can be taken up by the leaf. It is clearly illustrated in the Round Leaved Sundew, in which the blade curls up from its tip, or from one side or the other, or from the entire leaf margin so that the whole blade becomes cup-shaped.

pp. 120, 126–7

Does the leaf offer any enticement to prey? This is a question which naturally comes to mind, but which still awaits a definite answer. There

Drosera binata var. *dichotoma* 'Giant Type' magnified to show the gland-tipped tentacles and an unfurling leaf.

Drosera aliciae flowers. South African Sundews are noted for their pretty or showy flowers, which are often rather larger than those of the majority of species.

are no nectar glands, yet the bright drops of mucilage may themselves suggest nectar; or again, an alluring scent undetectable to the human nose may provide the key. This is speculation, but what is certain is that an extraordinary number of insects do choose to alight upon the leaves.

It would require a considerable monograph adequately to describe all the species in this genus. However, they are divisible into a number of sections, and in the following pages I will describe a selection of typical and outstanding plants. These have been divided into several categories for simplicity and convenience only; in no sense is this intended to represent a botanical system of classification.

Species forming winter resting buds

In the temperate parts of the Northern Hemisphere a group of Sundews occurs which die down in autumn to a green winter resting bud, or hibernaculum, in which form it is enabled to survive the winter. All European and most North American species belong to this group. In early autumn the plant starts to produce tiny modified leaves which often resemble embryo summer leaves in an arrested state of growth. These are many, closely packed and folded over one another to form a roundish object. The summer leaves gradually die, but this resting bud persists, anchored to the substratum by the now-dead roots. In the following spring new roots are formed, the resting bud opens and from its centre appears the new summer growth.

RIGHT Winter resting buds of *Drosera filiformis* ssp. *filiformis*.

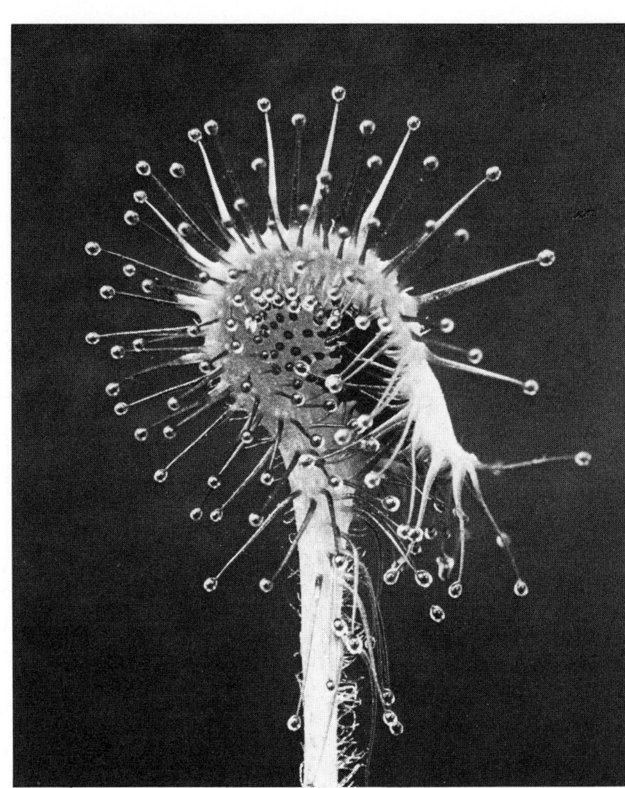

THE ROUND LEAVED SUNDEW *Drosera rotundifolia* is the most widely distributed species in the cooler temperate regions, and is found in North America, Europe, Russia and Asia. It occurs, often in vast numbers, in acid peat bogs, usually rooting amongst sphagnum moss. In fact, the presence of this moss almost invariably indicates that the sundew is not far away.

The leaves are arranged in a radical rosette. Their blades are round or nearly so, being usually a little wider than long, and they are slightly dished. Commonly about $\frac{1}{4}$ inch (6 mm) across, they may reach twice that size in shade. They are borne on flat stalks, which are normally about twice the length of the blade. When young, both blade and stalk are usually green, often becoming reddish with age, especially when exposed to sun. The stalks of the marginal tentacles are flat, and arise from conspicuously flared bases. Those of their immediate neighbours are also rather flat, but they become progressively rounder in cross-section as they near the wide central zone of the blade, where they are all short, upright and perfectly cylindrical.

The flower stem is from 2 to 6 inches (5–15 cm) long. It arises from the centre of the rosette, and is slender and smooth. The flowers are arranged in a raceme, which may be simple or once forked. They are small, seldom exceeding $\frac{1}{8}$ inch (3 mm) in diameter, and are usually closed, only opening at midday for a short time in bright sunlight. The

Drosera rotundifolia, BELOW shown natural size. LEFT to RIGHT The trap in action. The victim sticks to mucilage-tipped glands; other tentacles bend over and secure it. Later, part of the blade itself rolls over to enfold the victim. In the case of large prey all functional tentacles may be brought into action, and the entire leaf may be used to grip the fly.

p. 120

petals are normally white, pink forms occasionally being found in America.

Valued rather more in the past than in the present for its medicinal virtues, it is made much of in the old herbals, sometimes with caution. Thus we learn in the 1633 edition of Gerard's *New Herbal* that it has been recommended by others for use against consumption of the lungs, but we are warned that it cannot be taken with impunity for this purpose, 'for it hath also been observed, that they have sooner perished that used the distilled water hereof, than those that obstained from it.' It could, however, be used to both nourish and strengthen the body, and we are then given a recipe for a most delicious-sounding if exceedingly alcoholic liqueur. The plant could be remarkably troublesome on the farm, for 'sheep and other cattell, if they do but onely taste of it, are provoked to lust', but this apparently only affected females, which were thus given to a great increase in 'their vain opinion, without sense or reason', and we must assume that their opposites remained cooly aloof in the face of such wanton provocation. By 1797 the caustic juices of the plant were usefully employed to remove warts and corns, and the *Encyclopaedia Brittanica* of that year further confides that 'some ladies know how to mix the juice with milk, so as to make an innocent and safe application to remove freckles and sun-burn.'

The Sundews: Drosera

THE LOVE NEST SUNDEW *Drosera intermedia* is locally common in Europe, many parts of eastern North America, and also on high ground in Guiana, southern Brazil and Paraguay. Unlike the previous species the leaves are semi-erect and usually up to $1\frac{1}{2}$ inches (3·5 cm) long, though taller ones are found on the Gulf Coast Plain of the United States. But the main difference is in the blades, which are spoon-shaped, three to four times as long as broad, gradually tapering into the narrow stalk. The flowers are white, and very similar to those of the Round Leaved Sundew, but there are fewer to a stem, and this is much shorter and thicker and rises from the side, rather than from the centre of the rosette. It differs from other members of this group in having branching, semi-prostrate stems, which usually become submerged and rhizome-like in the ground. The winter buds remain attached to these, and ultimately extensive clumps sometimes result from single plants.

Favouring very wet conditions, it is most often found on peat over which water continuously seeps, on peat at the edge of bog streamlets, or even in shallow water in peaty puddles. It is seldom found in sphagnum, except when this is found floating as a fringe round the edge of bogland ponds; here it forms extensive floating carpets of brilliant red foliage, and is seen at its best. In sunlight, decorated with their glistening globules of dew, these carpets present one of the most arresting and unforgettable of sights.

The apex of the leafblade frequently curls inwards over a victim, holding it in a sandwich embrace, the entire blade often being doubled over. There would thus be no advantage in the sides of the blade inflexing, and in fact they have no power to do so.

THE GREAT, OR ENGLISH SUNDEW *Drosera anglica* occurs in Europe, North America and Japan. Despite its specific name, it is comparatively rare in England, though common enough in Scotland. It favours sopping blankets of sphagnum moss in which the water table is almost immediately below the surface.

Bearing a passing resemblance to *D. intermedia*, with which it is often confused, this is a much larger plant, the leaves often exceeding 3 inches (7·5 cm) in length. The blade is oblong and spoon-shaped, and merges so very gradually with the narrow stalk that it is difficult to tell where one ends and the other begins. In *D. intermedia* the base of the blade is more easily defined. While the tentacles in the latter species are dark crimson, in *D. anglica* they are bright red, contrasting vividly with the fresh pale green of the blade. The flower stems also differ in arising from the centre, rather than the side of the rosette, and are up to 6 inches (15 cm) tall. The flowers are also larger, measuring some $\frac{3}{10}$ inch (7·5 mm) across, the petals being white.

The leafblade has the same power and method of enfolding its prey as *D. intermedia*.

The English Sundew *Drosera anglica*. BELOW Natural size. See also page 217.

The Sundews: *Drosera*

Drosera linearis This unusual species has a very restricted and possibly decreasing range, being found only in North America in localities in the Great Lakes area, and from there upcountry in a narrow north-westerly band into Labrador. It differs from all the preceding species in requiring alkaline growing conditions, being found only in alkaline marl bogs. It is also rather different in appearance. The erect leafblades are extremely narrow, scarcely more than twice the width of the stalk, merging very gradually with the latter. The entire leaf seldom exceeds 1 inch (2·5 cm) in length. It is of a rather darker green than is common in *Drosera*, against which the reddish tentacles are less conspicuous. The flowers are small and white, and are borne on a raceme hardly taller than the leaves.

THE THREAD-LEAF SUNDEW *Drosera filiformis* is restricted in distribution to the east and south-east United States, where two subspecies occur. The leaves are quite different from those of other species, being thread-like, tapering at the apex. They unroll, fern-like, from reel-like buds in true circinate vernation. The stalk is so short that the heavily glandular linear blade appears to arise stalkless from the ground. It is an efficient trap, as may be seen from the numerous insects which stick to it. The blade does not have the power to enfold, which in this species would impair the efficiency of the trap. The flowers are borne on erect stems. They are rather large, of clear rose pink. The plant is generally found in moist, but not sopping, sandy peat.

Drosera filiformis ssp. *filiformis* is a pretty plant, easily recognizable, since the glands are red. The leaf can be 9½ inches (23·5 cm) long, and remains semi-erect. The flower is about ⅗ inch (15 mm) in diameter, and is generally of a deeper rose than in the following subspecies. Occurring in isolated parts of the east coastal area, it is especially common in New Jersey.

Drosera filiformis ssp. *tracyi* is a much larger plant than the preceding subspecies, but lacks much of its delicacy. The leaves are up to 20 inches (51 cm) in length, and are at first erect, but later tend to flop over, often gaining the support of neighbouring plants. The glands differ from ssp. *filiformis* in being green. The flowers also differ in being often as much as ¾ inch (2 cm) across, and are of pure rose pink. This is a very common plant in south Georgia and north Florida, and in the Gulf Coast area of Mississippi and Alabama.

A multitude of insect victims on a thread leaf sundew, *Drosera filiformis*. The photograph was taken in spring while the first summer leaves were unrolling, and it gives some idea of the value to the plant of its carnivorous diet. BELOW Natural size.

Other rosette-forming Sundews

SPOON-LEAF SUNDEW *Drosera spathulata* This species is found in Australia, Tasmania and New Zealand, and also in various parts of the Far East, including China, Japan, Taiwan, Hong Kong, Borneo and the Philippines. As one might expect of such a wide-ranging distribution, the plant occurs in many forms and varieties. In some forms the leaves are almost straight-sided and wedge-shaped, the end being rather blunt with rounded corners. In these the petiole merges almost imperceptibly with the blade. At the other extreme the petioles are narrow, while the blades are almost round. All have radical rosettes which produce tall stems of pink or white flowers. The following is a selection of forms:

'Kansai Type'. The rosette is up to 1½ inches (3·5 cm) in diameter. The leafblade is spoon-shaped, almost round, the upper half almost semi-circular, and nearly twice the length of the petiole, becoming suffused with red in sunlight. The tentacles are intense red and the scape, up to 9 inches (22·5 cm) high, may bear nine rose pink flowers about ¼ inch (6 mm) diameter. It occurs in Japan, in the Kansai and Chabu districts.

'New Zealand Type'. The rosette is up to 1¼ inches (3 cm) in diameter. The leafblade is rather similar to the Kansai Type, but rounder. The reddish scape is smooth except for scattered, white, somewhat wavy hairs. The white flower is ¼ inch (6 mm) across.

'Kanto Type'. The rosette reaches 1 inch (2·5 cm) in diameter. The leaf is wedge-shaped, with a rounded end, usually suffused with red, bearing tentacles of an intense red. The scape is up to 8 inches (20 cm) tall, with up to fourteen rose pink flowers ¼ inch (6 mm) in diameter. A variant has rosettes up to 1¼ inches (3 cm) across, and scapes up to 12 inches (30 cm) tall with as many as seventeen flowers. It occurs in Japan, especially in the Kanto district, and Australia.

A spoon leaf sundew, *Drosera spathulata* 'Kanto Type'. Four leafblades have folded over prey to varying extents. BELOW Natural size.

THE PINK SUNDEW *Drosera capillaris* ranges in North America from Virginia to east Texas in the coastal plain area where it is very common. It also occurs in Central America, Guiana, Venezuela, Colombia and Brazil. At first look this fibrous-rooted species may be mistaken for a vigorous *D. rotundifolia*, but it is evergreen and the round leaves are longer than wide. The rosette averages 1¼ inches (3 cm) in diameter, but an extra large form also occurs on the Gulf Coast. Recently a narrow-leaved form resembling *D. intermedia* was discovered in one bog in Florida. The flowers are usually pink, occasionally white, and about ¼ inch (6 mm) in diameter.

The Sundews: Drosera

Drosera burmanii The almost circular leafblades in this species are up to $1\frac{1}{2}$ inches (3·5 cm) across and narrow at the base, with a flat stalk of about the same length. The entire leaf is tinted a deep purplish red, and the outer tentacles are unusually long. This species is of particular interest in having marginal tentacles which are capable of unusually fast movement, of great use in securing larger insects before they can escape. Their movement can be very clearly seen with the naked eye, and the tentacle may complete its course through 180° in less than a minute.

There are up to eighteen flowers to a scape. The scape and sepals are purple-tinted, while the flower is white, about $\frac{3}{8}$ inch (1 cm) across.

This species is of fairly wide distribution in tropical parts of Asia and Australia, but it occurs near Sydney in warm temperate conditions.

The South African Sundews

The South African Sundews are of several different kinds, but as they include in their ranks some of the most impressive plants in the genus it is convenient to group our selection under one heading. Some possess unusually large leaves and tentacles, others are tall-growing, while some combine both qualities. The flowers can be showy too, and in *D. cistiflora* reach a diameter of nearly 2 inches (5 cm).

Rosetted South African Sundews

Drosera cuneifolia The rosette is just over 1 inch (2·5 cm) in diameter. The leaf is wedge-shaped and round ended, similar to, but proportionally wider than in *D. aliciae* and bearing intensely red tentacles. The deep lilac-pink flowers are about $\frac{1}{2}$ inch (1·3 cm) in diameter, and are borne on short scapes up to $3\frac{1}{2}$ inches (9 cm) high.

RIGHT Unfurling like a watch spring is the flowering scape of *Drosera aliciae*. BELOW Natural size. One leaf is clutching a fly. See also pages 10 and 124.

Drosera aliciae The rosette is up to 2 inches (5 cm) in diameter, and the leaves, dark green, wedge-shaped with blunt, rounded ends, have brilliant red tentacles. The leaves are up to three times longer than the widest point, and though similar to the *D. spathulata* 'Kanto Type', they are larger, and the tentacles continue almost to the base. The scape is up to 18 inches (46 cm) high, and the flowers, light purplish pink, are about $\frac{1}{2}$ inch (1·3 cm) in diameter.

Drosera natalensis The rosette is 2 inches (5 cm) in diameter, with spoon-shaped, almost round leaves very similar in form and colour to those of *D. spathulata* 'Kansai Type'. The scapes are about 12 inches (30 cm) tall, sometimes branched, with deep pink flowers $\frac{5}{16}$ inch (8 mm) diameter.

The Sundews: Drosera

Drosera capensis ABOVE Natural size, and OPPOSITE leaves encircling victims.

Stem-forming South African Sundews

CAPE SUNDEW *Drosera capensis* A large and showy sundew. The attractive leaves are loosely arranged in a rosette which is up to 6 inches (15 cm) in diameter. The leafblade is ribbon-like, commonly about $\frac{3}{16}$ inch (5 mm) wide and $1\frac{1}{2}$ inches (3·5 cm) long, terminating abruptly in a rounded point. The bright red tentacles contrast effectively with the fresh green foliage. The petiole is usually about the same length as the leaf, flat and unusually wide, about $\frac{1}{10}$ inch (2·5 mm). The plant is also peculiar in gradually forming almost woody, occasionally branchy stems which, like *Drosophyllum*, become trailing and retain the dead foliage of previous seasons. The scapes are about 1 foot (30 cm) high and bear up to twenty rosy pink flowers some $\frac{3}{4}$ inch (2 cm) in diameter. The leaf almost invariably enfolds its larger prey, the upper part neatly doubling over in a sandwich embrace once or often two times.

Drosera regia This giant sundew occurs only in the south-western Cape area, where it is rare. It is an impressive plant with the largest leaves in the genus. These are rolled in bud, uncurling to a length of from 10 to 18 inches (25–46 cm) in sun, or up to 28 inches (71 cm) in shade. They are erect and narrow, rising from a narrow base, and widening gradually towards the centre which is around $\frac{1}{3}$ inch (8 mm) wide. They then taper gradually again to a point. The flowering stem is about as long as the leaves, and bears a cluster of pale pink to deep purple flowers up to $1\frac{1}{2}$ inches (3·5 cm) across. The petals are narrow, terminating in a point. The plant is herbaceous, forming stems which are clothed with the dead foliage of previous years.

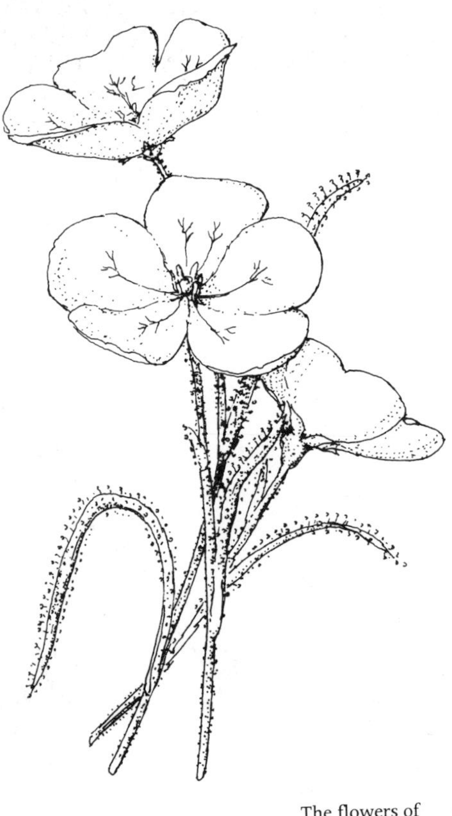

The flowers of *Drosera cistiflora*

THE CISTUS FLOWERED SUNDEW *Drosera cistiflora* is certainly one of the most beautiful of the *Droseras*. Its range is restricted to within about one hundred and fifty miles of Cape Town in any direction (according to J. D. Hooker), but within this area it is common. It forms leafy upright stems from about 6 inches to 1 foot (15–30 cm) long. The leaves are short-stalked, linear and about $\frac{1}{6}$ inch (4 mm) wide and between 2 and 4 inches (5 and 10 cm) long, light green with red tentacles. They fold over their prey in a similar fashion to *D. capensis*. The flowers are produced at the end of the stem. They are usually solitary, but are occasionally up to three-flowered, while a form is recorded with from three to six flowers.[14] They are amongst the largest in the genus, being about 2 inches (5 cm) in diameter and persist for about a fortnight. Commonly pale rose with a dark edge, they may be deeper pink, purple or a splendid scarlet. There is also a white variety, and a yellow variety is recorded.[15] When the seed matures, the stem dies, those in a lesser state of maturity remaining in growth. Growth normally takes place during autumn, winter and spring. In summer the ground often dries out, when the plant dies back to an underground rhizome from which it springs again with the coming of the autumn rain.

The Sundews

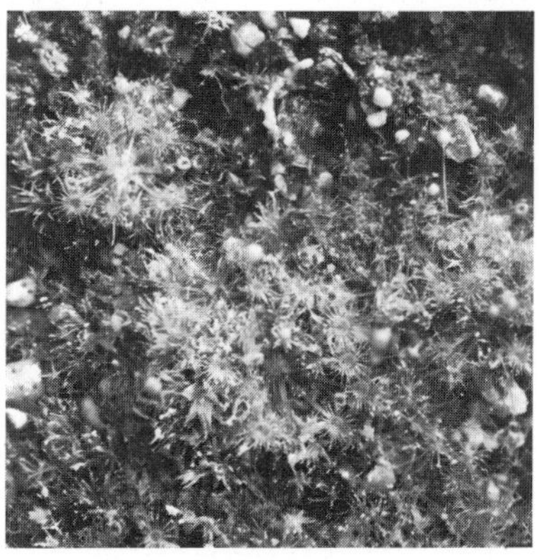

A group of *Drosera pygmaea*

The pygmy Sundews

The pygmy Sundews are found only in Australasia. They form neat rosettes of leaves which are small to minute in size. The flowers, too, may be tiny or surprisingly large in relation to the plant. They vary enormously amongst the species and can be white, pink or red, or more occasionally orange, apricot or even yellow. In bloom, some species are undoubtedly amongst the prettiest and most delightful plants in the whole genus.

The leafblades are dished and spoon-like. They are round or oval, and are borne on long, usually flattish petioles. One distinctive feature of the pygmies are the scale-like, whitish, almost transparent outgrowths, or stipules, at the base of these stalks. Stipules are present in other *Droseras*, but in this group they are highly developed and unusually large in relation to the leaf size. They are much toothed and deeply cleft, the precise form differing according to species. They die if the plant becomes dormant, but usually remain attached, retaining their shape and forming a sort of cone around the crown of the plant, which may play a major role in protecting it from the dehydrating effect of the hot sun.

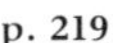

p. 219

Another feature unique to this group is the seasonal production of gemmae, their most common form of non-sexual reproduction. These are generally formed after the dry season with the coming of the rains. They then take the place of normal leaves and represent modifications of the blade. They are hard, simple and often scale-like in form. The point of attachment between the petiole and a gemma is narrow and fragile, and it soon breaks off and is scattered about by the rains. A bud then develops, tiny leaves are formed, and the roots appear next, the new plant often reaching maturity within two or three months time. In *D. nitidula* the gemmae are fishscale-like, and are arranged formally into a tiny saucer-shaped rosette, while in *D. pygmaea* they break off as they are formed, building up into a pile over the centre of the parent plant before they are splashed about by the rains.

There are many species, of which the following selection can only represent a cross-section. For a more complete list, the reader is referred to Rica Erickson's beautifully written and illustrated work on Australian carnivorous plants, *Plants of Prey*.[16]

Drosera nitidula group. The formation of reproductive gemmae is occurring in the large rosette to the right of centre, and gemmae are being scattered from the large rosette near the bottom left-hand corner of the picture.

Drosera pygmaea A pretty plant so minute that the leafblade with entire stalk is seldom larger than a single tentacle of *D. binata*. The blades are round, peltate (i.e. with the stem attached to the lower surface), up to $\frac{1}{16}$ inch (1·6 mm) in diameter, and become bright red in sun. The leafstalks are up to about $\frac{3}{16}$ inch (5 mm) long, rather flat, and usually greenish. The flowers are white, solitary, about $\frac{1}{10}$ inch (2·5 mm) in diameter and are borne on hair-like stems. The plant grows in damp places in south-east Australia, Tasmania and New Zealand, especially near the coast.

SHINING SUNDEW *Drosera nitidula* This plant is from Western Australia, where it inhabits wet sandy soils. It is rather larger than *D. pygmaea*, the rosette being up to $\frac{5}{8}$ inch (15 mm) in diameter, and the leaf stalk 2–3 times longer (3–5 cm). The leafblade is oval and reddish except in shade. There are several flowers, about $\frac{1}{8}$ inch (3 mm) in diameter, to a scape, and the three fleshy stigmas are crimson and provide attractive contrast to the white petals.

p. 158

Drosera dichrosepala The rosette of this plant is up to $\frac{3}{4}$ inch (2 cm) in diameter. The leaves are similar in form to *D. nitidula*, but fewer. The plant gradually forms a stem of about $1\frac{1}{2}$ inches (3·5 cm), to which the dead leaves remain attached. The white flowers are about $\frac{3}{8}$ inch (1 cm) in diameter with several to a scape, and the petals are rather narrow.

LEFT *Drosera dichrosepala* in flower

Pretty Sundew *Drosera pulchella*, much magnified. Though often minute, the leaves are efficient traps, catching correspondingly tiny insects.

PRETTY SUNDEW *Drosera pulchella* A lovely plant from south-west Australia. The flowers are large, up to $\frac{1}{3}$ inch (8 mm) in diameter, several to a scape. The petals are pale pink on the outside and deep pink within. The leafblade is round, usually green, though with red tentacles. The stalk is about twice as long, flat and rather wide. A red-flowered form which should be introduced to cultivation is recorded from a swamp in Albany where it grows in company with *Cephalotus*.

Drosera 'Bannister' Another beautiful large-flowered pygmy, this species has only recently been discovered at Bannister, south-west Australia, and awaits a Latin specific name. There are up to eight or so flowers to a scape. They are of soft rose, wide-petalled, with a green centre and five dark orange stamens. They are often as large as the leaf rosette itself, which is up to $\frac{3}{4}$ inch (2 cm) in diameter, the leafblades round to roundish oval and becoming reddish when exposed to sun. Their petioles are $1\frac{1}{2}$ times longer, and are green, flat, and rather wide. It differs from *D. pulchella* in the colour of the flowers and in the winter gemmae which are blackish purple.

DRUMMOND'S SUNDEW *Drosera drummondii* One of the finest in flower, there are up to ten flowers on a scape, each as much as $\frac{3}{4}$ inch (2 cm) or more in diameter, bright red with black centres and purple-black stems. The flower buds and sepals are covered with red down. The leafblades are narrow and elliptical, and are borne on rather long petioles, which may be four or five times as long. Western Australia.

COMMON SCARLET SUNDEW *Drosera glanduligera* This appears to be annual. The flowers are up to $\frac{5}{16}$ inch (8 mm) in diameter and are red with blackish centres. There are up to twenty on a scape. The leaves are a yellowish green and transversely elliptical (i.e. wider than long). In addition to Western Australia it is found in South Australia, Victoria and up to the centre of New South Wales.

The tuber-forming Sundews

The plants in this group are largely though not exclusively confined to the Australian continent. They grow in places which are normally subjected to extremely hot and dry summer conditions. During this period the plant dies down, but it is enabled to survive by means of the round tuber. With the coming of the winter rains this sends forth a shoot which either continues in growth above the ground as an aerial stem in the Fan-leaved and Rainbow Sundews, or terminates as it reaches the surface in a radical rosette in the rosetted tuber-formers. This underground shoot is clothed with scales which are in fact modified leaves (leaf scales). During the growing period the old tuber gradually becomes exhausted, but a new one is formed to its side.

The tuber is first formed in the following manner. After germinating the seedling develops a tap root with secondary roots in the normal manner, but some weeks afterwards it sends out a shoot from near the base of the stem. This is termed the 'dropper', and it is directed vertically downwards into the soil to a suitable depth, where the growing tip turns upwards and a tuber is formed which continues to enlarge until the advent of summer brings about the temporary cessation of growth.

Since the species are numerous and many are very similar to others, I will describe representative species of the three kinds.

Rosetted tuber-formers

The tubers of these plants may be $\frac{1}{2}$ inch (1·3 cm) or so in diameter, and the leaves are commonly of a larger size than are those of most rosette-forming sundews and are often fewer in number. These usually increase in size in a new spurt of growth after forming. There are fewer tentacles on the leaf than in other kinds, and those in the central area tend to be larger-stalked. When the new season's shoot is produced from the tuber it generally grows up the vertical passage left in the ground by the shoot of the previous year. In some species 'rhizoids'—root-like structures with the appearance and function of roots—arise from the base of the leaf scales on the underground stem, and a small parsnip-shaped horizontal root is produced at times from this position. This is used as an additional means of reproduction, each 'parsnip' able to form a shoot the following year, and to produce a tuber.

The Sundews: Drosera

SNOWY SUNDEW *Drosera macrophylla* This species occurs in Western Australia in sandy and loamy soils. The seven or eight leaves are round, narrowing towards their bases. They measure about $\frac{3}{4}$ inch (2 cm) across at flowering time, but afterwards increase in size often to a diameter of some $2\frac{1}{4}$ inches (5·7 cm). The white flowers are nearly 1 inch (2·5 cm) across, and are borne on several stems arising from the centre of the rosette. There are usually two to three to a stem, though they are occasionally single.

Drosera erythrorhiza Another Western Australian. The leaves are similar to those of *D. macrophylla*, but there are seldom more than five to a rosette, and they are smaller. The flowers are also similar, but several are borne on each of several stems arising from one single stem.

PAINTED SUNDEW *Drosera zonaria* Native to Western Australia, this species is so shy flowering that it was not seen in bloom till 1954, by Mr M. C. Russell at Guildford, WA. The great attraction is its leaves, of which there are many to a rosette. These are kidney-shaped, up to $\frac{2}{5}$ inch (1 cm) across, and edged beautifully with crimson. They have rather long stalks which tend to be hidden by the overlap of inner leafblades. The flowers are similar to those in *D. erythrorhiza*. It grows in sharply drained sand.

Drosera hamiltonii Found in permanently boggy places this has no tuber as it does not have to withstand a drought season. The leaves are continuously produced and distinctive, measuring up to 1 inch (2·5 cm) long. They are wedge-shaped and rather narrow, with rounded apexes, reddish and sparsely glandular. The flowers are huge for the size of plant and a beautiful lilac-purple, up to $1\frac{1}{2}$ inches (3·5 cm) across, with sometimes a dozen on a scape up to 18 inches (45 cm) long. Very rare in nature, this species occurs in the extreme south of Western Australia, chiefly in *Cephalotus* bogs.

The rainbow sundews

These plants either have tough, very narrow, wiry stems, which are erect and self-supporting, or they may be tall, numbers often arching in a mass over scrub for support, when, combined with the irridescence created by their thousands of small leaves in the sunshine, the overall effect has been compared with rainbows.

Some, such as the Bridal Rainbow (*D. macrantha*) are climbers, using their long-stemmed gluey leaves to gain extra support. In all the leaves are small. In the first year, while the plant is young, these are usually arranged in a radical rosette, but as the plant matures it produces an annual stem. The leafblades in the rosette stage are usually round or elliptical, the axis of the ellipse being at right angles to the leafblade.

Drosera hamiltonii: a rarity in nature but not difficult to grow. Easily recognized by its distinctive foliage, it produces exceptionally large lilac-purple flowers.

The stem leaves may be of similar form, but in many species they are half-moon shaped, the rounded half forming the base, and both corners are drawn out into two narrow lobes suggesting lynx ears, which gradually terminate in points. The latter are edged with tentacles, terminating in a single one. The stalks of the stem leaves are long and narrow. In many species secondary, smaller leaves develop in the leaf axils. The tubers of most species are small, seldom larger than pea seeds.

Drosera peltata, a typical Rainbow Sundew. ABOVE Natural size. The unusually long outer tentacles are able to ensnare what might seem abnormally large prey for the size of the leaf, as shown in the bottom left of the picture OPPOSITE.

Drosera peltata This is of wide distribution, occurring in India, China, Japan, and south-east Asia, Malaysia, and eastern Australia. The leaves of the rosette are round and peltate, about ⅛ inch (3 mm) across. The stem of the flowering plant is erect and narrow, up to about 10 inches (25·5 cm) high, and its leaves are cupped, the two corners terminating in narrow pointed lobes. The flowers are white, up to ½ inch (1·3 cm) in diameter, several to many to a raceme.

Drosera auriculata Ranging through eastern Australia from Brisbane to South Australia, it also occurs in Tasmania and New Zealand where it is common in wet ground. This is very similar to and easily confused with *D. peltata*. The flowers are slightly larger and the plant may reach 12 inches (30 cm) or more in height, but the main botanical difference is in its smooth black dotted sepals (in *D. peltata* they are hairy) and in the different seed shape.

SWAMP RAINBOW *Drosera heterophylla* A species from Western Australia which is unusual in that the attractive white or pale pink flowers have eight or more petals. The stem is erect, up to 12 inches (30 cm) tall, and clothed with narrow scale-leaves. The shield-shaped leaves are about ⅛ inch (3 mm) across, their petioles being rather shorter than in most species. There may be five flowers, up to ¾ inch (2 cm) in diameter, with rather narrow petals.

Drosera sulphurea This unusual and attractive yellow-flowered species is found in peat or sphagnum bogs in the central region of the extreme south of Western Australia, often amongst *Cephalotus*. It grows to some 16 inches (40 cm) high. The stem is narrow and erect with scale-leaves on its lower part. The leaves are in threes; they are green, shield-shaped, about ⅙ inch (4 mm) wide, with two pointed lobes. The flowers are brilliant yellow, up to 1 inch (2·5 cm) across, and several to a spray. Another species with similarly coloured flowers and habitat is *D. subhirtella*, which is, however, easily identified by the reddish coloration of its foliage.

MODEST RAINBOW *Drosera modesta* This is a shade-loving climbing plant from Western Australia which may reach about 3 feet (90 cm) in height. The stem is very narrow, covered with small non-carnivorous

glandular hairs. In common with the leaves it is yellowish. The latter are about $\frac{1}{8}$ inch (3 mm) across, shield-shaped, with two pointed lobes. The dozen or so flowers are white, $\frac{5}{8}$ inch (1·5 cm) across, with narrow oval petals.

BRIDAL RAINBOW *Drosera macrantha* A tall climbing plant from south-western Australia, where it occurs in a variety of soils. The flowers are over 1 inch (2·5 cm) in diameter, scented, white or pink and very showy, the petals broadly oval, nearly round. The leaves are round, up to $\frac{3}{8}$ inch (1 cm) in diameter, on long petioles. They and the stem are yellowish green.

Drosera gigantea An erect species growing to 40 inches (1 m) high from Western Australia, often occurring in masses in wet ground. The stems and leaves may be green, or tinted with maroon to a greater or lesser extent. The stem has scale-leaves on its lower part, the leaves are shield-shaped with pointed lobes. The white flowers are very numerous, about $\frac{1}{2}$ inch (1·3 cm) in diameter, and are borne in loose panicles.

Drosera menziesii Another Western Australian, and very attractive with reddish or maroon foliage and flowers which may be any shade of pink, to crimson or dark red. Up to 14 inches (35 cm) high, it is erect, free-standing or sometimes climbing. The round leaves are up to $\frac{1}{8}$ inch (3 mm) across, peltate, the petioles often rather long. The flowers are sometimes single, more often several to a raceme. They are about 1 inch (2·5 cm) in diameter with roundish petals. Various forms occur, in habitats ranging from swamps to sandy well-drained soils.

The fan-leaved sundews

This is a group of three species and their forms. There is usually a basal rosette from which arise one or more leafy stems. The flowering scape may arise from these, or separately. The leafblade is usually fan-shaped, though this it not always so in the basal rosette. Its stalk is wide, and the base clasps the stem conspicuously. All come from Western Australia.

Drosera stolonifera There are many forms in this species, foliage shape and size varying considerably, as does also its coloration, which may range from green to purple. The habit is equally variable. In most but not all forms the flowering scape rises directly from the rosette and bears no leaves. It is branching and often bears numerous white flowers. The species is readily identified from other fan-leaved species by the stem leaves being arranged in threes or fours rather than singly.

BRANCHED SUNDEW *Drosera ramellosa* In this species one to several foliage stems arising from the rosette bear yellow-green fan-leaves up to $\frac{1}{4}$ inch (6 mm) long, arranged alternately. The scapes are often single-flowered and leafless, $\frac{1}{2}$–4 inches (1·3–10 cm) long, bearing small white flowers.

Drosera platypoda The erect stem is up to 10 inches (25 cm) tall, the leaves are singly borne, fan-shaped and about $\frac{2}{5}$ inch (10 mm) long. The scape is sometimes branched and bears white flowers up to $\frac{3}{4}$ inch (2 cm) in diameter.

The North Queensland Sundews

The following two species differ from the several others which occur in the tropical climate of North Queensland. Though of dissimilar shape, the leafblades in both are unusually thin, excepting at the rather stout midrib. They are of a rather pale green, and the mucilage-secreting tentacles are unusually sparsely scattered.

Drosera schizandra

Drosera adelae This species occurs in the hills in the Rockingham Bay and Dalrymple's Creek areas and on Hinchinbrook Island, where it occurs in boggy places beneath trees.

The leaves are narrowly lance-shaped and are said to reach 8 inches (20 cm) or more in length in the wild. In cultivated plants they may not exceed half this measurement. They are semi-upright, and crowded together at the top of a gradually growing stem which becomes clothed with the remains of dead foliage. They are pale green, membranous, with a pronounced midrib, narrowing towards the base, with a short stem which is covered with short woolly hair. The tentacles are rather short and sparsely scattered.

The flowers are amongst the most inconspicuous and dull in the genus. The green sepals and brownish petals are both about $\frac{1}{8}$ inch (3 mm) long and pointed.

Drosera schizandra This species is found in bogs on Mt Bartle Frere. The leaves are arranged in a rosette, and are said to reach a maximum of 4 inches (10 cm) long in nature, but in cultivated plants are often less than half the size. They are typically wedge-shaped, the wide apex being either entirely rounded, or, as is often the case in nature, notched at the centre. They are pale green, membranous, and the tentacles are sparsely distributed. The midrib is not conspicuous from above. The flowers can be whitish and as unimpressive as in *D. adelae*, but there is a magnificent form with rich red petals. These are wedge-shaped, about 5 mm long, with rounded ends. The sepals are rather shorter, green, and pointed.

The Sundews: Drosera

The fork-leaved Sundews

Varieties of *Drosera binata* are easily recognized from all other *Droseras* by the narrow forking leafblade, which may divide once to several times, so that at its simplest the leaf may somewhat recall a wishbone or at its most complicated a much divided antler. In all its divisions the leaf is narrow, and each terminal division tapers to a point. For this reason, the latter limbs are conveniently referred to as 'points'. Each is furnished at its apex with a crown of three or four extra long tentacles. These divisions are all circinate (tightly rolled in the bud) as in the ferns, and they unroll much as we see in the young leaves of Bracken (*Pteridium aquilinum*). The leaves are large in all varieties and forms, and those of *D. binata dichotoma* can in certain conditions, as when growing amongst reeds, considerably exceed those of *D. regia* in length. The species occurs in eastern Australia, varying from a northern limit on Fraser Island, Queensland, southwards through New South Wales to the coast of Victoria and westwards to the south-east of South Australia. It is also found in Tasmania and New Zealand. It inhabits a variety of places from mountain bogs to coastal swamps, always requiring an acid, soggy soil which is permanently, rather than periodically, wet.

The flowers are white, occasionally pink, and are borne on long, many flowered racemes which generally fork into two, occasionally three. These are produced in abundance while the plant is in growth.

Though a variable species, there are very distinct varieties of which all others may be considered intergrading types, forms or hybrids, listed below.

After its single non-carnivorous first leaves a seedling will produce a number of round leaves which though tiny, are very similar to those of the Round Leaved Sundew. Succeeding leaves gradually change shape from round through oval, half-moon and quarter-moon, till they gradually form the 'Y' that one sees in *D. binata* 'T Form'. The leaf does not normally divide more until it has reached maturity.

Drosera binata 'T Form' is so called because the linear leaves fork only once. This would be more accurately described as a variety, and as the two divisions of the blade curve into an upward and often vertical ascent, 'Y variety' would have been a more descriptive term. The leaves are commonly up to 12 inches (30 cm) in length, the petiole usually being about twice the length of the leafblade. The leafblade may be up to $\frac{1}{10}$ (2·5 mm) in width, scarcely wider than the stalk. Both are of a deep olive green, often becoming suffused with red as they age. The tentacles are deep red. The white flowers are about $\frac{1}{2}$ inch (1·3 cm) across the racemes often two-branched and reaching some 19 inches (48 cm) in

Drosera binata 'T Form', magnified to show the gland-tipped tentacles and unrolling of young leafblades.

Drosera binata 'T Form', whole plant. Half natural size.

height. This form becomes dormant for one or two months in winter.

Though the smallest distinct variety of the species, this is a beautiful plant. Not only is the form of the leaf attractive in itself but the intensely red tentacles give a rosy glow to the clump and the numerous droplets of mucilage are well displayed against this background.

It has been grown in the greenhouses of Europe and America for well over a century, and is still by far the commonest of the four varieties in cultivation. Not unnaturally, it has often been regarded as the typical *D. binata* (a belief long shared by the author) and was referred to simply as *D. binata*. It is, however, of comparatively rare occurrence in nature and, though it probably resembles a common ancestor of the four forms here described, it is, in the author's view, most probably an offshoot of *D. binata* var. *dichotoma* 'Small Type. It is, however, distinct, and comes true from seed.

There is in cultivation another 'T Form' of larger growth, with wider leafblades and green-stalked, red-glanded tentacles. A coarser plant, this is probably of hybrid origin or a form of *D. binata dichotoma*. It is not to be confused with *D. binata* C.V., a cultivar of hybrid origin which occasionally produces three-pointed leaves.

Drosera

Drosera binata var. *dichotoma* 'Giant Type' in spring leaf. The leaves produced later are considerably longer—see page 191.

Drosera binata var. *dichotoma* Placed under this name are what appear to be two distinctly different varieties of the species. It is perhaps unfortunate that the same name has been applied to both, for this infers that one is merely a variant of the other, which I am inclined to doubt. In both, the leafblade of the mature plant is most commonly twice divided, giving a four-pointed pattern as shown above. But this is by no means invariable, for branching, especially in the larger form, is somewhat irregular even in one leaf, so that one may find individuals with from two to occasionally as many as eight points. Both plants are also alike in becoming dormant for a very short period in winter, but here the similarities end.

'Small Type'. This is very like *D. binata* 'T Form' in every detail except in the division of the leaf as described above, in its pale green colour, and in the green to amber-green coloration of the tentacles. This is the 'dichotoma' of most common occurrence in nature, and will understandably be regarded by many as the true plant. Yet this is questionable, since it seems to have been unknown in the greenhouses of the Northern Hemisphere till a few years ago, when

Mr Stephen Clemesha sent plants to America from Australia. Prior to that time the following was the only dichotomous type with which I was acquainted, or of which I can find earlier record.

'Giant Type'. This is decidedly different from 'Small Type' and from all other known varieties and forms of *Drosera binata*, and it may have resulted from a genetical mutation. From Charles Darwin's description, it was clearly this plant that he was so grateful to receive from his friend Lady Dorothy Nevill while researching into the carnivorous nature of sundews. It is much larger in all its parts. The entire leaf is up to 23 inches (58 cm) long, the stalk being up to twice the length of the leafblade, the span of which is normally up to about 7 inches (18 cm). The two primary divisions of the blade are often about $\frac{1}{5}$ inch (5 mm) wide in the mature plant, the secondary ones usually being about $\frac{1}{8}$ inch (3 mm) wide. The stalks of the tentacles are normally green or greenish amber in colour, their glands being amber to reddish, so that from a distance the leaf appears green rather than reddish. The blades themselves are yellowish green and never acquire the red tinge which is an attractive additional feature of the older foliage in the other forms and varieties. The giant stature of this plant, though impressive, loses much of the grace one finds in the other plants.

pp. 123, 191

The flowering stem is rather stout, and rises well clear of the foliage before it usually divides into two, three or even four racemes which may rise to a height of some 30 inches (76 cm). The flowers are numerous, and about 1 inch (2·5 cm) in diameter. Winter dormancy is generally rather short, seldom exceeding a month in greenhouse plants.

Drosera binata var. *multifida* In this most attractive variety the leaves commonly divide into six to eight points. It differs from the two *D. binata dichotoma* types in that the divisions of the leaves are more constant and more regular (i.e. the divisions of the left hand of the blade are likely to repeat those of the right). In other respects it closely resembles the 'T Form' except that the tentacles tend to be of a more vivid and darker red. It is of fairly common occurrence in the warmer parts of the *D. binata* range. Two-pronged leaves are always produced in immature plants, and in mature plants often in the spring and less often at other times. Unless subjected to cold temperatures in winter this form differs from others in continuing to grow throughout the year. Two fine forms of this variety which have also been introduced to cultivation are worth mention.

'Extrema'. In this form the leafblade is yet more divided, and there may be anything between fourteen and thirty-six points to a single leaf, giving the whole plant a ferny appearance. The red coloration of the tentacles and the tinting of the leaves is extremely

A fourteen-pointed leaf of *Drosera binata* var. *multifida* 'Extrema' unfurling. The nine-pointed leaf behind could easily be mistaken for the typical *multifida*. Leaves with fewer divisions are common in winter and spring.

marked. It is a tropical plant, and a native of Stradbroke Island near Brisbane, Queensland, where it is unfortunately now threatened by mineral extraction operations.

'Pink Form'. This pretty pink-flowered form is rather uncommon in nature. In the clone in cultivation the leaves are commonly divided into six to eight points. However, it appears to be rather closer to the typical form of *D. binata multifida* in other respects than to *D. binata dichotoma*. It differs in having a period of winter dormancy, but this may not exceed three weeks.

8 The Spring Traps

The Venus Fly Trap and Waterwheel Plant are closely related, though the former is a terrestrial plant while the latter is aquatic. Though they belong to the same family as the Sundews (Droseraceae) they employ a decidedly more dramatic technique in securing their prey. Their traps consist of twin valves bringing to mind those of an empty sea mussel. These are held ajar like an open spring trap. A victim entering the compass of the valves trips a trigger mechanism, whereupon the valves snap together with often surprising speed like a pair of jaws, and the animal is securely held within.

The Venus Fly Trap: Dionaea

Dionaea muscipula (dy-o-*nee*-er). Fam. Droseraceae

When seen for the first time, the sudden closing of the jaw-like lobes of this plant is a startling experience, and it may not be surprising that it appears to have been the first plant to have been suspected of carnivory; this very shortly after it was first recorded in the eighteenth century. It is the only species in its genus and, despite the undoubted ingenuity and efficiency of its trap, seems to be on the verge of extinction, for its limited range in the coastal area of south-east North Carolina and in the adjoining land in the east coast corner of South Carolina is fast diminishing. Here it favours a damp but not sopping soil largely of sand with a small proportion of peat, and is clearly exacting in its requirements, for attempts to introduce it to other apparently similar habitats beyond its range have failed.

The first known record is that of Arthur Dobbs, Governor of North Carolina, who in a letter of 1763 to Peter Collinson calls it 'the great wonder of the vegetable world'. He likens it to 'an iron spring fox trap', remarking that 'on anything touching the leaves, or falling between them, they instantly close like a spring trap, and confine any insect or anything that falls between them', but he makes no conclusion as to a possible reason for this behaviour.

In 1768 the first live plants were introduced to England by William Young, the Queen's Botanist. Some of these were seen by John Ellis, a Fellow of the Royal Society, and an amateur botanist. He strongly

The Venus Fly Trap *Dionaea muscipula*. The silhouette of a trapped fly can be seen in the closed leaf on the right.

suspected the carnivorous nature of the plant, sending a letter to Linnaeus to this effect together with dried specimens. In his account he even suggests that the lobes may secrete sweet liquor to attract insects, which we now know to be the case, though he assumed that this was secreted by what are in fact the digestive glands. Since the Swedish botanist was only provided with dried material, it is understandable that he should have remained unconvinced by what must have then seemed all too imaginative a hypothesis. In allusion to its beauty he named it *Dionaea*, one of the Greek names for Venus. Some thirty years later the great American traveller-botanist, William Bartram, shows himself to have been in no doubt that the plants he came across were carnivorous, for in his masterpiece of 1793, *Travels in North and South Carolina, Georgia and Florida*, he has the following to say:

> But admirable are the properties of the extraordinary *Dionaea muscipula*! A great extent on each side of the serpentine riverlet is occupied by those sportive vegetables—let us advance to the spot in which nature has seated them. Astonishing production! See the incarnate lobes expanding, how gay and sportive they appear! Ready on the spring to intrap incautious deluded insects! What artifice! There behold one of the leaves just closed upon a struggling fly; another has gotten a worm; its hold is sure, its prey can never escape—carnivorous vegetable!

By the middle of the nineteenth century many botanists were convinced of the carnivorous character of the trap, but strong suspicion can prove nothing, and it was not until the early seventies that Darwin conducted his experiments on what he considered to be 'one of the most wonderful plants in the world', proving beyond doubt that *Dionaea* both digests its victims and absorbs the resultant fluids into its system.

The foliage is in a rosette arising from a short unbranching rhizome which is clothed with the succulent bases of the petioles of previous leaves. The leafblade is in the form of the twin-lobed trap. This is borne on a petiole which is often flat and leaf-like in the spring, somewhat wedge-shaped, widening towards its end. The sides then curve in, forming a deep central notch from which the pronounced midrib emerges as a short stalk supporting the central spine of the trap (A). These supporting leaves are usually prostrate, or nearly so, and the rosette in spring seldom exceeds 3 inches (7·5 cm) in diameter, and the petiole is from half to twice the length of the trap.

Flowering takes place in early summer, and immediately following this another type of petiole is usually produced. These are flat, but rather narrower than the spring kind, or even stalk-like (B and C). They differ also in being always semi-decumbent to erect. They are commonly three to four times the length of the trap, the entire leaf being usually between $2\frac{1}{2}$ and 5 inches (6·5–13 cm) in length, though it can reach $6\frac{1}{2}$

RIGHT *Dionaea muscipula* trap. The trigger hairs—in this case four to each lobe—are clearly visible, and the presence of the microscopic glands is shown by the speckled surface. The nectary zone is the darker area below the base of the spines.

A: spring-type leaf-stalk or petiole. B and C: typical summer-type petioles.

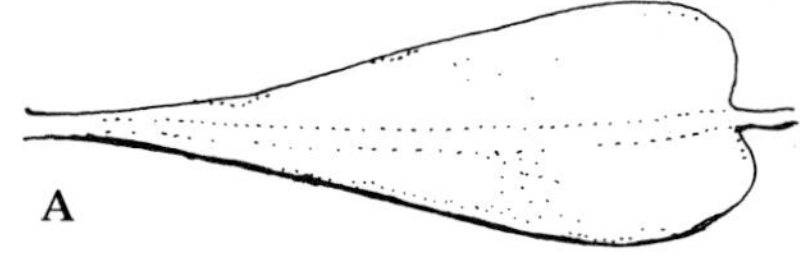

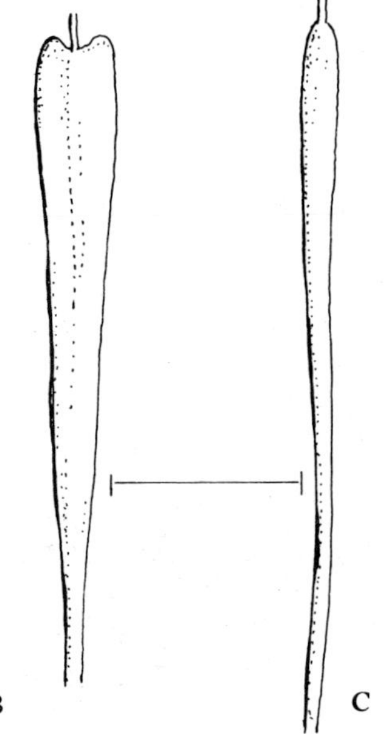

substratum, its stalk being almost entirely buried. The scape is up to 10 inches (25 cm) high and bears several lilac flowers which appear rather large for the plant. The upper lip is very small, nearly horizontal, but slightly upturned at its rounded apex. The lower lip is about five times longer, its apron somewhat flared, merging gradually with the large palate. The colour is of a deeper tone here, and it is topped with a light yellow patch and often a whitish touch just below. The spur curves downwards and projects from the base.

In addition to those on the stolons, there are one or two traps on the buried part of the leafstalk. The sides are extended to form a funnel-like entrance, which is lined with about ten rows of stout glandular hairs.

Utricularia sandersonii This delicately pretty South African species is in constant flower for the greater part of the year. The leaves are between an $\frac{1}{8}$ and $\frac{1}{4}$ inch (3–6 mm) long, pale green, spoon-shaped and round-edged. The scape is up to 2 inches (5 cm) long and carries up to seven flowers of palest Wisteria blue, which are about $\frac{1}{4}$ inch long by $\frac{1}{2}$ inch (6 mm by 1·3 cm) wide. The upper lip is deeply forked into two narrow, round-ended segments, each marked with a central violet streak. The lower lip is twice as long, and forms a flat but spreading apron, the lower half of which is semi-circular with a wavy edge. It is tinted with violet around the palate, which is touched with yellow-green.

Utricularia novae-zealandiae As denoted by the specific name, this is a New Zealander. The leaves are light green, up to $\frac{1}{2}$ inch (1·3 cm) long, rather narrow, becoming gradually wider towards the rounded apex. The scape is up to a foot (30 cm) high. The flowers are in opposite pairs. The upper lip is dark violet, very small, oblong and nearly vertical. The lower lip is of a lighter violet and is inclined forwards at right angles to the upper one. It is fan-shaped, slightly reflexed at the sides and about $\frac{3}{4}$ inch (2 cm) long. The palate has two vertical ridges which are rich yellow bordered in dark violet. The spur is half as long as the flower, thick, blunt-ended and down-pointing.

FAIRY APRONS *Utricularia dichotoma* This is an entirely Australian species occurring in Queensland, New South Wales, Victoria, southern Australia and Tasmania. The leaves are up to a $\frac{1}{4}$ inch (6 mm) long, pale green, and narrowly elliptical. The scapes are up to 12 inches (30 cm) high and bear either one or two pairs of opposite flowers, or these may be in a whorl of three. These are showy, up to $\frac{3}{4}$ inch (2 cm) across, ranging from lilac to more commonly violet, or purple in colour. The upper lip is small and nearly vertical, while the lower lip is large, flared and apron-like, its lower half being semi-circular. The palate is twice grooved, forming three ridges which are brilliant yellow. The trap has a long beak, and has in addition a pair of lateral wings the ends of which are divided into several pointed, finger-like segments.

LEFT *Sarracenia* x 'Evendine'. A horticultural hybrid raised by the author. It is notable for the varied coloration of the pitchers, ranging from a golden green ground while young, ageing to a rich dark red, and conspicuously veined. These may reach 20 inches (51 cm) in height. The medium red flowers are rather large. Lineage: *S. leucophylla* x (*S. flava* x *S. purpurea*).

The Bladderworts: Utricularia

REDCOATS *Utricularia menziesii* This Western Australian is unusual not only in the bright red colour of its curious flowers, but in being one of that very small group that forms corm-like tubers, and which in this species are hardly larger than a grain of wheat. By means of this organ it is enabled to survive the dry period. With the coming of the rains its dormancy is broken and it sends forth a cluster of foliage. These leaves are up to $\frac{3}{8}$ inch (1 cm) long and are rather narrow, widening to the rounded apex. A little time afterwards the scapes emerge, which are reddish and up to $2\frac{1}{2}$ inches (6·5 cm) long. Each terminates in a bract from which a short pedicel rises, bearing the solitary red flower. Its upper lip is wedge-shaped, slightly notched at the centre to form two rounded lobes, and is somewhat bent backwards. The lower lip is about twice as big, and about $\frac{2}{5}$ inch (10 mm) in length and width. Its palate is tall and large, blocking the mouth, five-ridged and bright yellow. Perhaps the most striking feature is the extra long spur, which is twice the length of the lower lip and three quarters its width. It has a blunt rounded end.

The stolons are not of the runner type we have seen but are short, serving as anchoring devices for the tuber. The bladders are borne singly on the ends of long stalks which radiate from the tuber, some downwards, some sideways and some upwards, though the traps on these never emerge from the surface of the soil. The prominent beak curves down in front of the entrance to just below the base of the trap. There are two pairs of wings, the lateral pair arising from the sides of the beak just over the entrance, and sloping downwards, terminating in a number of finger-like lobes, while the other pair arise from the base of the trap and extend horizontally forwards, so that these, together with the lateral wings and beak, form a sort of protective structure around the entrance. This probably prevents the entry of particles of the substratum and may tend to retain water in suspension around the entrance while keeping spaces open through which small animals can pass.

RIGHT The flowering scapes of *Utricularia sandersonii*. ABOVE Natural size.

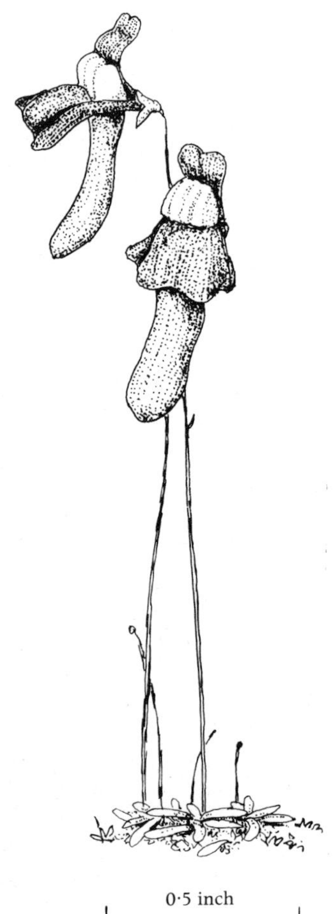

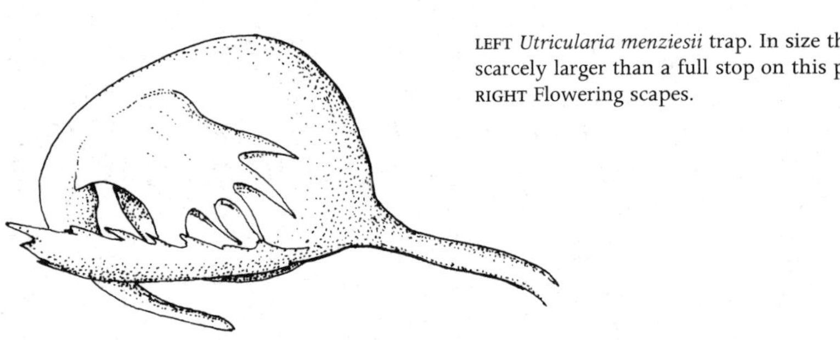

LEFT *Utricularia menziesii* trap. In size this is scarcely larger than a full stop on this page. RIGHT Flowering scapes.

The Pink Petticoats: Polypompholyx

Polypompholyx (pol-i-pom-fol-ix) Fam. Lentibulariaceae
There are currently two recognized species in this Australian genus; both are annuals. They are distinguished from *Utricularia* by the calyx, which is divided into four lobes. The flowers are pink. The upper lip is deeply divided into two small, narrow lobes while the lower one is up to six times the size, deeply divided into three flared lobes, the outer two being rather shorter than the central one, the entire lip much resembling a sleeved petticoat. There is a blunt spur. The leaves radiate from the base of the plant, and are small and narrow, becoming broader towards the rounded apex.

The trap

The trap differs in some ways from those of *Utricularia*. There are two lateral wings. The stalk becomes somewhat inflated as it nears the trap. The beak is wide and forked, and is closely applied to the inflated stem,

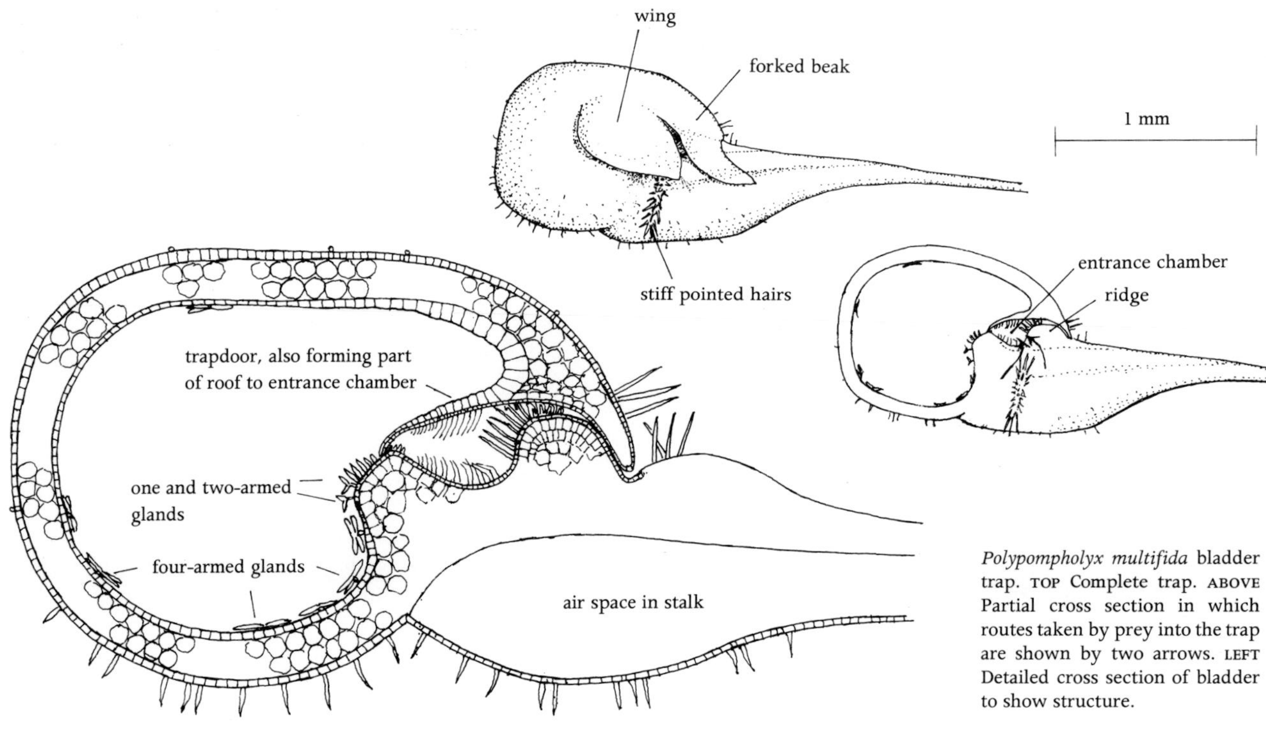

Polypompholyx multifida bladder trap. TOP Complete trap. ABOVE Partial cross section in which routes taken by prey into the trap are shown by two arrows. LEFT Detailed cross section of bladder to show structure.

Flowers of *Polypompholyx multifida*

so that entry is blocked from the entire front but not from both sides, on each of which the wing and the beak combine to form funnel-like entrances. Each funnel is divided by a comb of pointed hairs on the stalk, and leads on each side to an individual entrance vestibule which is separated from its neighbour firstly by a ridge on the stem closely applied to the underside of the beak, followed by another comb of stiff hairs. The ceiling of the two vestibules is made up of the beak and of the inwardly-inclined door itself (see diagram). Both the floors of the two vestibules and their ceilings are covered with tapering hairs which point inwards, and must urge visitors forwards to the bladder.

Polypompholyx multifida The scapes are between 4 and 9 inches (10–23 cm) long and rather slender for the size of flower, of which there are usually several. Popularly known in Australia as Pink Petticoats, these are rose pink, and are borne on slender pedicels of varying lengths. The yellow palate has several ribs and is bordered beneath and at its sides with red. The three-lobed lower lip is about 1 inch (2·5 cm) wide, each lobe being notched or lobed at its end. It is always a surprise to see these very splendid and liberally-produced blooms supported, as far as is evident from the leaves, by so minute a plant, but the foliage gives no indication as to the extent of the underground stolons with their numerous traps. This species occurs only in Western Australia, principally on the south-western coastal plain.

PINK FAN *Polypompholyx tenella* This is in effect a miniature form of the above species, the flower being about $\frac{1}{4}$ inch (6 mm) across, but there are only one or two to the scape. Like *P. multifida*, it is found in Western Australia, but it also occurs in Victoria and South Australia.

10

How to grow Carnivorous Plants

Carnivorous plants are amongst the most satisfying of plants to grow. Quite contrary to a still-lingering belief, the majority are of easy cultivation. Few lack beauty, indeed many possess this to a high degree, as we see in the elegant lines and often rich coloration of the trumpet pitchers, in the exquisitely bejewelled foliage of the sundews and the flowers of many. But previously, sufficient attention was not paid to the outstanding role that a small number may play in the household as useful fly catchers, the laurels for which must undoubtedly go to *Sarracenia flava*. A large pitcher of this species not only accommodates several thousand houseflies, but takes saucy wasps and nasty bluebottles into the bargain! Food should never be provided for any species; they will catch sufficient for their needs in the most apparently fly-free of houses and greenhouses, always providing chemical fly controls are not in use, but these should be rendered superfluous by the plants themselves. The application of fertilizers as an alternative to live insects can result in the death of your plants.

Cultivation indoors

As window plants

A few carnivorous plants are suitable material for growing in most houses without the use of a special terrarium (see page 185). As conditions of light, temperature and humidity tend to vary from house to house and from room to room, it is clearly not possible to guarantee that a particular plant will thrive in a particular house. Also, most like rather cooler room temperatures in winter than at other times, which are rather more easily provided in Europe and Australasia than in North America where much higher room temperatures are favoured. Some trial and error may be necessary to determine what will grow best.

In my own house the following grow successfully in sunny south-facing windows: *Sarracenia purpurea venosa, S. psittacina* and *S.* x *catesbaei, Pinguicula caudata, P. mexicana, Drosera spathulata* forms, *D.*

The flower of *Sarracenia minor*. The stamens are visible between the petals and the umbrella-shaped pistil.

aliciae, *D. natalensis*, *D. cuneifolia*, *Dionaea muscipula*, and *Utricularia lateriflora*. In rather less sun *Utricularia prehensilis*, grown as a terrestrial rather than as an aquatic plant, and *U. dichotoma* will thrive. All these plants probably benefit from the rather cool night time temperatures they experience in Britain in winter, which may descend to the low fifties Fahrenheit (10–11°C). In the sunniest windows *Sarracenia flava* thrives. Apart from its fine pitchers this proves an extremely useful fly-catcher, but the pitchers are inclined to become drawn and weak where sunlight is more limited, nectar secretion is then less, and it attracts less prey in consequence. *Drosera binata* forms can usually be depended upon to do well wherever *S. flava* does, and indicates a lack of light by developing long weak leaf stalks or petioles. In rooms where a minimum temperature of 65°F (18·3°C) can be maintained, *Drosera adelae* is often successful. This is a useful plant, for, disliking too much sunlight, it will often succeed in sunless windows providing the light is good, and the same may be said of many of the terrestrial *Utricularias*.

If any one of these plants is grown singly its pot should be placed in soft water in a pot-saucer at least a size larger than the pot in order to supply adequate water to the plant and some humidity in the air around the plant. When several are to be grown in one window I prefer to place them in a narrow plant trough about 6 or 7 inches (15–18 cm) wide and about the same depth. I use a black trough, and the plants are in black polythene pots, shortened where necessary so that all are of a uniform height less than that of the trough. In this way the pots are inconspicuous. As in the greenhouse, the saucers and troughs should be kept dry during the winter, though the compost must always remain damp.

This black plant trough, in which thrive *Sarracenia psittacina*, *S. purpurea venosa* and *Pinguicula caudata*, is on the author's dining room window sill.

Under artificial light

Away from windows or where there is little or no sun, you may still grow these plants under fluorescent lights. Specially made units are available for house plants, usually consisting of a tray for pots, while columns support an overhead canopy with the concealed lights. Similar structures are not difficult to make. Lighted shelves can be constructed, the lighting units being attached to the lower side of each shelf and concealed by timber battens along the front. The inside of the batten and shelf should be painted white to reflect maximum light, for there will be little room for a reflector. Alternatively, units complete with reflectors may be suspended over a 'growing table'. Whatever system you devise, it is advisable always to use two-tube units, and always install reflectors where practical. The tubes should be of the daylight type, or one of those specially designed for horticultural use.

The plants need to be rather close to the light source and they should be well established and rooted in their pots. In these conditions the plants would benefit from a light spraying of the foliage during the growing period. *Drosera, Pinguicula* and terrestrial *Utricularia* should be within 12 inches (30 cm) of the tubes, while *Sarracenias* must be even closer. *S. leucophylla, alata, rubra* and *minor* should be within 6 inches (15 cm), and *S. flava* within 8 inches (20 cm) of the tubes. With these erect-pitchered species this is not always a very easy thing to manage, and the best plant for the purpose is undoubtedly the decumbent-pitchered *S. purpurea venosa*, which must be within 8 inches (20 cm) of the source. Switch on for sixteen hours in daytime in summer, gradually lowering to nine hours lighting by mid-winter.

The terrarium

This provides ideal growing conditions for a variety of carnivorous plants. It can be easily made from an aquarium topped by a rather wider sheet of glass which may be moved a little to one side to adjust ventilation. The size will depend upon what you intend to grow.

Compost One part of horticultural sand to one part of moistened moss peat is a good medium. This should be a minimum of 5 inches (13 cm) deep, but it is a good plan to slope it up to the back, in this way providing wetter and drier conditions to suit the tastes of individual plants.

Watering This should be done with care, using pure soft water and a can with a rose. Though the compost must be very moist, it must not be soaking wet, and if when the finger is pressed $\frac{1}{4}$ inch (6 mm) into the compost water is seen to form, this is an indication that there is too much water.

Position and light If you can, place the terrarium on a well-lit or east-facing window when light may well be sufficient for the plants you intend to grow, but avoid full sunlight which will heat it excessively. If there is not enough light or if you place it away from the window, supplementary lighting will be required, consisting of fluorescent lights placed on the top of the glass cover, and reflectors. These should be two-tube fixtures, and one such unit should be sufficient, providing it is as near as possible to the length of the aquarium.

Allow sixteen hours light in summer, gradually lowering to eight to ten hours in winter. The shorter winter photoperiod suits those plants from cooler climates, while those from warmer places prefer ten hours.

Planting Some thought should be given to arrangement, and to the ultimate size of each plant. It is easiest to plant the rosette-forming *Droseras* bare-rooted in the immature state, but if potted and mature they should be gently knocked out of their containers, and enough compost removed from the terrarium to accommodate that on their roots. *Drosera adelae* and *D. schizandra* need to be planted in pure live sphagnum moss, and a hole 4 or 5 inches (10–13 cm) in depth and width should be excavated and filled with the moss. The same treatment should be given to any plant for which a sphagnum-based compost is recommended (for example, many of the South American *Utricularias*). In such humidity sphagnum growth is inclined to be excessive, but can usually be kept under control with occasional firming.

Greenhouse cultivation

You do not need a special greenhouse in order to grow carnivorous plants. On the contrary, the majority will mix quite happily with other greenhouse subjects ranging from fuchsias to tomatoes, always providing their essential requirements are catered for. The obvious exception would be a cactus house, since it would be inadvisable here to maintain the high humidity required by carnivorous plants.

The greenhouse is best sited in a light, sunny position, for while it is true that the majority of carnivorous plants abhor fierce sun, this can be reduced as required by shading materials, and most appreciate light. It should not be exposed to strong winds which will remove considerable heat and can also lift and break glass from the framework. It should be of strong construction, of timber and glass or metal and glass. Polythene houses are much cheaper, but they do suffer from considerable condensation drip and high humidity in winter, which encourages fungus diseases, while heat loss is excessive. The house should be a minimum of 8 feet (2·4 m) wide; ideally 10 feet (3 m), for this allows room for a 3 feet (90 cm) wide path. It should have adequate ventilators. The path must be paved with bricks, slabs or concrete, thus providing a suitable surface for 'damping-down'. It is worth investing in roll-down slatted sunblinds for the outside of the glass. There should be guttering, and the rainwater should be piped to adequate storage butts or tanks to ensure a supply of soft water through dry periods. Large open storage tanks within greenhouses are not advised (except in the case of the stovehouse) as these lead to too high a humidity in winter.

The choice of a heating system is very largely a matter of circumstance, and individual choice. Convector heaters burning paraffin or natural gas are adequate for the small coolhouse or warmhouse and quite harmless to plants, providing there is some ventilation. There is a snag here if you have automatic ventilation, for complete closure can result in the build-up of harmful fumes, but this problem can be overcome if you fix a wooden strip $\frac{3}{4}$ inch (2 cm) thick under the ventilator to prevent it closing completely. Such heaters are not suitable for the stovehouse where the ventilators are normally not opened. Electric tubular and fan heaters are rather more expensive to run. They are, however, suitable for all kinds of house, as are hot water systems heated by oil fired or solid fuel boilers, and oil fired hot air systems in which the fumes are discharged externally via a chimney. Unfortunately, most of the systems use electricity in one way or another, which prevents them from working during a power cut. It is therefore a wise precaution to invest in a supply of cheap paraffin burners for such an emergency, though it must be remembered that if these are used temporarily in the stovehouse the ventilators must be opened. All systems should be thermostatically controlled (not yet possible with smaller paraffin convectors).

Considered in terms of maximum and minimum temperatures there are four types of greenhouse with which we are concerned here: the coolhouse, the coldhouse, the warmhouse and the stovehouse. The coolhouse, is, for most purposes, by far the more useful, depending, of course, on what one wishes to grow. It is relatively cheap to heat, and in it may be grown the widest range of those carnivorous plants which are at present in cultivation.

The coolhouse

Minimum winter night temperature 40°F (4·4°C) rising to 50–55°F (10–12·7°C) by day. Summer minimums 45°F (7·2°C) by night, 55° (12·7°C) by day. The path should be about 3 feet (90 cm) wide to ensure comfortable working, though it would need to be as little as 2 feet (61 cm) wide in an 8 feet (2·4 m) wide house. There should be staging, the supporting legs of which must be upon firm bases. At the far end of the house an eave-to-eave shelf, about 12 inches (30 cm) wide, will be found most useful for plants which require plenty of sun, such as *Drosophyllum* and *Byblis*. Watering is best done by what we here call the 'tray system'. The alternatives are non-metallic large greenhouse gravel trays 2 inches (5 cm) deep or garden pool-lining material placed on flat asbestos sheeting or marine plywood, the edges supported by timber strips. Whichever you use, trays should be placed on the staging, which must be absolutely level, and the potted or boxed plants then placed in them. The chief advantages of this system are that it is a very simple method of watering, and it raises the humidity of the house. If the trays are filled to their full depth you can go away for a few days with reasonable confidence that the plants will not dry out, but as a normal practice they should only be half filled during the growing season, because the higher water table does not permanently suit many plants. In autumn, winter, and early spring the trays are left dry, for at this time high humidity is not required, and in fact encourages fungal disease, but the trays may still be used for watering, only sufficient being poured in for the pots to completely absorb, the object being to keep the compost damp but not soggy. A minority of carnivorous plants are not suited to this treatment and should be stood in the traditional gravel tray.

High temperatures in hot weather cannot easily be avoided, and this is especially so in warm temperate regions. The danger of leaf-burn in the upper pitchers of *Sarracenia* and *Darlingtonia* can be avoided, providing shading and humidity are sufficient, even though the temperature may climb to 100°F(37·7°C). Even if paint shading has been put on the glass, additional shading in the form of the roll-on slat-type blinds will be advisable. Ventilation also should be increased, but as this will lower the humidity of the house, it should be combined when possible with frequent damping-down of the path.

The coldhouse

This house is kept free of frost, with a winter night minimum temperature of 34°F(1·1°C). To ensure this, a reliable thermostatically controlled heater should be used if frost sensitive subjects are grown. Heating is cheap, since this is used only during cold weather, but the range of plants which may be grown is limited, and so most people will find it more convenient to put these plants in the cool greenhouse. Subjects suitable for the coldhouse are all the *Sarracenias, Darlingtonia, Drosera filiformis* var. *tracyi,* and the hardier forms of *D. binata.*

Apart from heating, the set-up recommended for the house is exactly the same as for the coolhouse.

The warmhouse

Winter minimum night temperature should be 55°F (12·7°C), winter day minimum 60–65°F (15·5–18·3°C). Summer night minimum 65°F (18·3°C), summer day minimum 70°F (21°C). Except that heating will be necessary through much of the summer in cooler climates, the warm greenhouse is arranged and managed as for the cool greenhouse.

The stovehouse

Winter minimum night temperature 60°F(15·5°C), winter day minimum 70°F (21°C). Summer night minimum 70°F (21°C) and summer day minimum 75–80°F (23·8–26·6°C). The arrangement of the house can be similar to that of the cool and warm greenhouses with the differences that the tray system of watering must on no account be used for *Nepenthes,* which requires rapid run-out of all excess water after watering. If *Nepenthes* is to be the main subject, it will be wise to provide staging on one side of the house only, so that the other may be entirely paved, providing a standing ground for the faster-growing types which rapidly become tall. High humidity is necessary, for the stovehouse caters for plants which are at home in the tropical rain forests. To achieve this, damping and syringing down with water is necessary, a practice fully explained in the cultural information for *Nepenthes* (page 203). Ventilation is normally neither necessary nor advisable, except in exceptional circumstances or in very warm and humid climates. In addition to *Nepenthes,* most of the epiphytic and

Pitchers of the Cobra Lily *Darlingtonia californica.* The spiral twisting of the pitcher during growth can be clearly seen, as can the numerous windows on the dome and rear walls.

similar species of *Utricularia* from South America will thrive in this house, as will *Aldrovanda*, but few if any sticky-glanded carnivorous plants are suitable, for they dislike the frequent wetting of their foliage.

Cultivation out of doors

A fair proportion of the carnivorous plants in cultivation are suitable for growing out of doors. They fall into two categories: those that may remain outside for their entire life, and those which must be brought into a frost-free or warm environment for the winter. Plants in the first category are many if one lives in the favoured localities of California or New South Wales, while in the colder parts of North America and northern Europe very little other than *Sarracenia purpurea* ssp. *purpurea*, and a few hibernaculum-forming species of *Pinguicula* and *Drosera* are likely to succeed. The obvious advantage of growing plants in the open is that it saves valuable greenhouse or indoor space, or obviates the need for having a greenhouse at all. Its chief disadvantages are that evaporation of water is heavy, calling for adequate soft water supplies, that foliage may be subject to damage by wind and hail, or by children and animals.

The selected site should be as sheltered as possible from prevailing and high winds. It should be sunny, but in warmer regions mid-day shade from a judiciously-placed tree or from lath shading on a supporting structure will be an advantage, and the presence of nearby trees will help to cool the air. Avoid hot places near sun-exposed paving and house walls.

One method is to grow the plants in pots, using the tray watering system described on page 187, excepting that there is no need to empty the tray of water in the winter; indeed, this would allow free access for slugs and other creeping and crawling pests. Another is to construct an artificial peat bog, which may be small or large, and may be of two basic types.

One sort of bog is constructed like an artificial pond. I like this to be between 12 and 18 inches (30–46 cm) deep, which allows room for sufficient water to cut down the frequency of summer watering. Use either an ordinary cheap plastic or, better, a black butyl rubber pool liner. Excavate to the shape required—a nearly oval to nearly round shape will be found more satisfactory than a less formal one—and make sure that the surface is levelled around the margin. Place the liner not quite taut over the 'pool', anchoring its edges with heavy stones or concrete blocks as weights. Now pour sufficient pure soft water into the centre to weigh it down heavily. Gradually let the liner down, lifting and replacing the weights as you go, till it reaches the bottom. Cut two small holes about $\frac{1}{8}$ inch (3 mm) in diameter, one in each side wall, 6 inches (15 cm) down. These allow gradual surface drainage,

In flower, and growing out of doors in southern England, is *Drosera binata* var. *dichotoma* 'Giant Type'.

which is important for those plants objecting to very wet conditions, while preserving a reasonably high water table. Now almost fill the structure with previously moistened moss peat. Press this down firmly as you go; all the water in the bottom should be absorbed before you have proceeded very far. When your are 1½ inches (3·5 cm) from the top, stop and thoroughly soak the peat with applications from the rose of a can. Now fill in the surface with a mixture of moss peat and broken live sphagnum moss in equal volumes, and soak again. If the garden soil surrounding the bog is of a limey or alkaline nature it will be necessary to ensure that it does not come in contact with the bog soil, and it will be advisable to bring the plastic liner sides a fraction above the soil level. The edges of the liner may be held in place by carefully placed natural-looking rocks or occasional stepping stones, while trailing plants may conceal the spaces between, and this type of bog can very easily blend into the lower parts of the rock garden, or in the peat garden.

Another type of bog may form a pocket at the side of a large artificial pool, or form an island within it, always providing the water is not alkaline. The sides are retained by non-calcareous stones, unmortared bricks or concrete blocks which are easily concealed by the planting of suitable water weeds. The pocket or island is filled entirely with moist moss peat, the surface of which should rise from about 2–6 inches (5–15 cm) or more above water level. That well known amateur gardener, the late Mrs Amy Bond, constructed a bog of this type some twenty years ago at the side of a large pond in her garden at Burford House in Somerset, England. Amongst other plants she grew was a splendid colony of *Sarracenia purpurea purpurea*, while the upright pitchers of *S. flava* 'Maxima' formed part of the bordering planting.

In arranging the plants, it is a good rule to keep plants of similar habit together. A mixture of all sizes and habits is seldom attractive, and in any event, low growing sun-lovers like *Dionaea* and many sundews should not be shaded by the taller pitcher plants. The latter are best grouped so that they do not shade other plants, unless this is actually desirable for a particular species.

With regard to outdoor growing, the experience of correspondents from many parts of the world coupled with my own leads me to the following conclusions. In very warm areas with hot summers *Sarracenias* will thrive outside, even where summer humidity is as low as 40 per cent, though shade should be provided at mid-day. Where night temperatures reach a low of 32°F (0°C) in winter they may be left outside with safety for the entire year, though there is some evidence that most, and possibly all, will tolerate a minimum down to 25°F (−3·8°C). Undoubtedly several will tolerate even lower temperatures, and there is room for more recorded experiment. In my own part of south-west England, where winter minimums normally reach about 26°F (−3·3°C), but have recently reached a low of 12°F (−11°C), both *S. purpurea venosa* and *S. flava* prove hardy, as, of course, does *S.* x *catesbaei*, and—somewhat against the 'rules'—at least one form of *S. rubra*. *S. leucophylla* and *S. minor* seem from one trial only to be tender. Of the *Droseras* I successfully grow *D. anglica, rotundifolia, linearis,* and *filiformis* ssp. *filiformis* out of doors. *Dionaea* will survive only mild winters in Britain, and the evidence points to its being hardy where winter lows do not fall below 28°F (−2·2°C). *Pinguicula grandiflora, P. grandiflora* ssp. *rosea* and *P. vulgaris* will also all grow outside if shaded from hot sun, but I believe the latter at least might be expected to fail in warm temperate regions.

Mr Philip Sheridan of Arlington, Virginia, reports usual winter minimum temperatures of 20°F (−6·6°C), but these can fall as low as 0°F (−17·7°C), yet he grows *Sarracenias, Dionaea* and *Pinguicula caerulea* successfully for the entire year out of doors. These are grown in bogs made from 3 foot (1 m) deep children's pools. When winter comes, he covers the entire bog to a depth of 3 or 4 inches (7·5–10 cm) with sphagnum moss. In spring the moss is removed, and the *Dionaeas* appear fresh and green. There may be slight rot amongst the *Pinguicula* leaves, but they come through the winter safely. He tried this method with *Drosera binata* 'T form' in the 1978 winter, and it survived, and he is putting the plant to further tests.

In my experience, slugs and snails attracted to the moisture of the bog can be a nuisance, and it is wise to lay bait around its perimeter, especially during spring, when they can attack the young growth of *Sarracenias* and *Pinguicula*. One advantage of the island bog is that these pests are prevented access by the water.

Containers and materials

Before talking about the requirements of individual plants, it would be wise to discuss briefly suitable containers, water and potting materials.

Pots

For most purposes plastic pots are preferable to clay. The latter too readily become covered with algae and moss when standing in water, and when *not* so covered they require more frequent watering due to evaporation from their porous sides. Pot sizes are usually given as a measurement, and this refers to the inner maximum diameter in the case of round pots and to the width if they are square. The common pot is approximately as deep as it is wide, and we here refer to it as full length. The dwarf, or half-pot as it is sometimes called, is rather less than three quarters as deep as it is wide. The seed pan is rather less than half as deep as wide, and as it is not always easy to buy these days, it may be necessary to substitute a half-sized seed box, or a dwarf pot.

Containers and materials

Saucers

Special saucers are manufactured for pots; thus a 5 inch (13 cm) pot may stand in a matching 5 inch (13 cm) saucer, but where they are used for carnivorous plants these should always be at least a size larger than the pots in order to provide a large surface area for evaporation, to keep up humidity levels.

Seed boxes

These should always be of plastic with drainage holes.

Propagators

Unheated: These are of various kinds and sizes. The tray type consists of a plastic tray in which may be placed pots or seed boxes, surmounted by a clear rigid polystyrene cover with ventilators. It is important to make sure that the tray is *not* provided with drainage holes. Cheap but very useful polystyrene propagator covers are also available shaped to fit over plastic seed boxes, while round propagator covers are made to fit several sizes of pot.

Water

This must be soft, as hard water is a slow poison to many carnivorous plants and causes sphagnum and peat to decay. But it must not have been softened by the conventional water softener, for it then often contains salt which is poisonous to the plants. Rainwater is ideal. Distilled water is also excellent, though expensive if used on anything but a small scale. On a larger scale, if rainwater is not available, it may well be worth installing a water de-ionizing unit or an RO unit (reverse osmosis purified water unit). Boiled water is also satisfactory if it is allowed to stand.

Sand

This should be sharp so as to ensure an open medium. The individual grains should be angular rather than smooth. About 65 per cent should be between an $\frac{1}{8}$ and $\frac{1}{16}$ inch (3–1·6 mm) in size, the rest being finer. It must not be an alkaline kind; a quartz (silica) type such as silver sand can be used with confidence providing it is pure, as is usually the case with 'nurserymens' sands'. Sea sand must never be used, for it contains salt, is too fine, and too smooth. Builders' sands are unreliable and often dirty, and some grit-sands can be too predominantly coarse for cultivation purposes.

Peat

The only peat suitable is granulated moss peat. This has been gradually formed in acid bogs from sphagnum moss, and is acid in reaction. Other types of peat are not suitable, especially sedge peat, which is often alkaline and a slow poison to many carnivorous plants.

Containers and materials

Sphagnum moss

Three types are referred to in the cultural information: live, long-fibre, and shredded long-fibre sphagnum. The long-fibre types are not available in many countries, and suitable substitute materials or composts have been given where appropriate. Live sphagnum can be bought from a few suppliers, but if it is possible to collect it from the wild it is always best to select that which grows in the wet rather than sopping parts of bogs, and which is as free as possible from grass and other herbage. There are many different species of sphagnum, and the best are those which are rather thick and succulent-looking in their growing parts, and which when pulled up have rather long stems. These remain open in texture and do not easily compact when in a pot. Do not use mosses other than sphagnum; you will certainly lose your plants.

Perlite

It is most important to use a horticultural grade of this material. Others usually contain impurities harmful to the plants. This is easily obtained by the amateur grower in North America, but this is not at present always so in Europe. However, to my knowledge one British nurseryman supplies a *Sarracenia* compost which is peat, sand and Perlite-based, and this may be the case in your own area.

John Innes Compost No 2

This is available commercially in many countries. It consists of seven parts of sterilized loam, three parts granulated peat, two parts horticultural sand. Added to each cubic yard of the mixture are 10 lb. (4·5 kg) John Innes base fertilizer, and 2 lb. (910 g) ground chalk. The base fertilizer is made up of two parts by *weight* of hoof and horn, two of superphosphate of lime, and one of sulphate of potash. Other good mixed general potting composts may be suitable, providing they are loam-based.

Crocking

Generally speaking, it is unnecessary to place drainage crocks in the bottoms of the pots unless specifically advised to do so for a particular plant. Where crocks are necessary the best material consists of broken pieces of clay pot. These should be placed with their convex surfaces uppermost.

Species cultivation

The following list is arranged in the order of the genera in the previous chapters, and includes additional species, forms, varieties and hybrids. It includes all of what I believe to be the most desirable carnivorous plants in cultivation today, but excludes many that I either consider of botanical interest only, or which have so far failed to prosper in artificial conditions. Also excluded are those which are as yet difficult or impossible to obtain, and unproven in cultivation. With the steadily rising interest in carnivorous plants the number grown will increase, but in the majority of cases you can be guided by following the same methods suited to the most closely related species.

It should be noted that where watering is followed by the word 'tray' this refers to the tray system of watering described previously on page 187.

The Sun Pitchers

Until recently *Heliamphora* was exceedingly rare in cultivation, and was generally considered to be a very difficult plant to grow. But it is now becoming clear that cultivation need not be difficult, providing a correct technique is adopted. Mr Joseph A. Mazrimas of California, one of the greatest authorities on the cultivation of carnivorous plants, has kindly provided me with the following cultural information: 'I grow three species: *H. nutans*, *minor* and *heterodoxa*. I believe these three are p. 21 the only ones in cultivation at this time. The remarks below pertain to all three species except where noted.'

General cultivation Plants are grown in plastic or clay pots which are half-filled with horticultural perlite of average size $\frac{1}{5}$ inch (5 mm), and filled to the top with living sphagnum moss. The moss is used to support the rhizome by packing it snugly against the sides of the pot. A 50/50 mixture of chopped sphagnum and perlite can also be used as a substitute. A shallow saucer or dish can be placed under the pot and kept full at all times during the growing season.

Propagation Plants are propagated by division of the rhizome, using a sharp knife to cut a section containing a small cluster of pitchers.

Species cultivation

Heliamphora plants have a scarcity of roots which are long brownish-white and uniformly thick, $\frac{1}{12}$ inch (2 mm) diameter, 4–8 inches (10–20 cm) long. They are also very brittle, and break very easily when bent, and so great care must be exercised to remove the cut piece from the mother plant without breaking the roots. Usually only one or two roots accompany the cut piece. If the roots should break off, then the cutting must be treated like an unrooted plant. Usually, new roots will grow from the rhizome if a plastic bag is used to retain high humidity around the pitcher cluster during the rooting process, but it takes one to two months for several roots to form. Some of the pitchers may wither during this time, but that is insignificant just as long as several pitchers remain green and turgid.

Feeding I use Osmocote 14–14–14, a slow release pelleted fertilizer. I use $\frac{1}{4}$ teaspoon (1·25 ml) per 4 inch (10 cm) pot and 1 teaspoon (5 ml) per 8 inch (20 cm) pot. Plants are fed in March and August only.

Watering I use de-ionized water, and plants are watered every day with copious amounts during the growing season, which in California is February to October. Watering is less during winter when growth ceases.

Temperature Summer range is 50–78°F (10–25·5°C). Winter range is 42–69°F (5·5–20·5°C). At no time should the temperature exceed 78°F (25·5°C) for prolonged periods of time. If edges of the new leaves start to turn brown, then the temperature is too high or the humidity is too low. Normal humidity is about 50 per cent.

To Mr Mazrimas' information it should be added that Osmocote 14–14–14 is unfortunately not available everywhere, and those growing *Heliamphora* for the first time would be better advised to use *no* fertilizer than to experiment with others which could result in the loss of their plants. I would add that I personally apply no fertilizer. Though I give my plants full sun I drench them with soft water spray at least daily in summer, more occasionally in winter.

The Trumpet Pitchers

Given correct treatment and healthy material almost all *Sarracenia* species and most hybrids are exceptionally easy to grow. Failures are usually due to faulty methods of cultivation or to starting with inferior material. Always buy plants which are already well-established and healthy from a reliable grower. Plants grubbed up from the wild are sold in both North America and Europe as leafless rhizomes, and are usually in poor condition. They often carry pests which the plants seem to tolerate in nature, but which too often lead to their hasty demise in cultivation, not always without adding one or two of one's other plants

The strongly delineated veins are an attractive feature of *Sarracenia* x *popei*, a natural hybrid.

to their list of victims before they attract attention. Quite apart from this, the wholesale collection of such plants from the wild is a serious contributory cause to their decline in numbers and already threatens the continued existence of some species.

General cultivation Containers vary in size and type according to the plant and are given below under the species or hybrid. Pot in spring or early summer when in full growth: winter or late summer potting may result in losses. The compost should be either three parts broken live or long-fibre sphagnum moss to three parts moss peat and one part of sand, or six parts moss peat, two parts perlite, and one part of sand. Water by the tray system. They like sun, but light shading is advisable, and they should be in a cool greenhouse except for *S. purpurea* ssp. *purpurea* which is best grown out of doors, but otherwise given the same treatment. In many parts of the warmer temperate regions, in southern Europe, Australia and the southern USA, most if not all may be grown out of doors along similar lines.

Comments Do not let the plants form thick clumps, normally divide every two or three years. Hygiene is important to prevent disease. The pitchers in most species will die from the top downwards at the end of the season and the dead part should be periodically cut off so as to leave the live part intact, the latter being of value to the plant. When the whole leaf is dead, it should be carefully removed from the base.

Species cultivation

Propagation In spring, you can propagate *Sarracenias* by division. Split the rhizomes during early pitcher growth with a clean cut. Select those with several roots attached.

If division is to be by rhizome cuttings, select a plant in spring with a long rhizome and cut off as much as possible of this while still allowing the main plant to have sufficient roots for growth. Divide the piece of rhizome into lengths between $\frac{1}{2}$ and 1 inch (1·3–2·5 cm) long, cutting with a clean sharp knife. Each should have at least two roots attached, and the cut should show white tissue. A rhizome showing dead brown tissue should be shortened sufficiently to remove it. Pot these sections up in normal *Sarracenia* compost, allowing the top of the rhizome to be exposed, but butting a little compost against each cut end. Place in a water tray in good light but shaded from sun. Cool greenhouse. Shoots may take anything from weeks to months to appear. Some rhizomes may rot, and these should be removed immediately. Only introduce to full sun in following year.

Seed should be fresh, collected the previous autumn. Sow in February in cool greenhouse, using *Sarracenia* compost in seed pan, small dwarf pot or plastic seed box, and placing in water tray. Cover seeds with minutely thin layers of moss peat by scattering dry moss peat through fine kitchen sieve till seeds disappear from view, then damping this with hand sprayer. Germination usually takes six to eight weeks. At beginning of July prick out into dwarf pots, spacing an inch (2·5 cm) or more apart, using same compost. I find fresh seed almost invariably germinates, but if it is not fresh, refrigeration may help. In this case mix some with damp sphagnum moss, place in a plastic bag, and put in the non-freezing area of your refrigerator for six weeks before sowing. Maturity is reached some six years later.

Sooty mildew can scarcely be classed as a disease since it does not hurt the plant. Here it is seen on the upper tube and lid of *Sarracenia flava* where the fungus feeds upon the nectar. It is common in poorly ventilated greenhouses subject to strong sunlight and high temperatures, seldom becoming a nuisance in well ventilated, lightly shaded houses. Most fungicides will kill the spores.

Pests and diseases In cultivation they have remarkably few pests, unless rhizomes are lifted from the wild, when unseen larvae feeding upon their interiors are often imported at the same time. Greenfly often infest the immature unopened pitchers, and as these will ruin their form they should be removed with the fingers or by any garden aphicide if infestation is widespread. Whitefly seem to affect only *S. rubra* ssp. *alabamensis*, in my experience. A systematic insecticide will usually dispose of these.

The only serious disease liable to be troublesome to the beginner is the common grey mould *Botrytis cinerea*, which is evident as patches of grey or brownish-grey mould. Prevention is better than cure, for once its mycelia have penetrated the interior of the rhizome there is little that will arrest its progress in destroying the plant. In a clump, drastic cutting out of affected rhizomes may save the remainder. Chief causes are too high a humidity in winter, too little light and bad hygiene. Systematic removal of all dead material from the plants is important, for it is on dead parts that the fungus starts. These, and especially infected parts, should be removed from the house and burnt. Those species and hybrids which form dense clumps and thus tend to have ill-lighted areas amongst the pitchers are most often affected, *S. rubra* being perhaps the most prone, and it is a good plan to divide this before it clumps to any degree, as it is also with *S. purpurea, psittacina,* x *courtii* and the like. The disease should not be a problem in summer if conditions are right, and in winter and early spring humidity should be kept as low as possible: no water in the trays, and the compost only just damp. Good ventilation is also important, and will help to rid the air of floating fungal spores. Pitchers with the slightest sign of mould should be cut off well below the infection or removed altogether. A monthly spray during this period with a suitable systemic fungicide such as Benlate is a very effective preventative.

The species The following should be treated as described in the general cultivation notes. The recommended pot sizes are for full length pots unless otherwise noted.

S. flava: 5 inch (13 cm) pot

S. flava var. *rugelii* and var. 'Maxima': 6 inch (15 cm) pot

S. leucophylla and *S. rubra* ssp. *jonesii*: 5 inch (13 cm) pot

S. alata, S. minor, S. oreophila: 4½ inch (11 cm) pot

All *S. rubra* types except ssp. *jonesii*: 4½ inch (11 cm) pot

S. purpurea and subspecies: 5 inch (13 cm) dwarf pot. This ensures a high water table in summer which the plants appreciate.

S. psittacina: 5 inch (13 cm) dwarf pot. The whole potted plant should be completely immersed in clear soft water during the whole winter, so that its foliage is entirely submerged. Remove from water only as early growth becomes evident in spring. This is unnecessary in climates where it is grown out of doors.

The Pale Pitcher Plant *Sarracenia alata* in flower, showing the distinctive form of the petals.

Species cultivation

The Cobra Lily

pp. 70, 189

Darlingtonia californica requires different growing conditions to either *Heliamphora* or *Sarracenia*. For the beginner it would be wise to start with a mature plant, which should be planted in the spring or very early summer.

General cultivation Use a 6 or 7 inch (15 or 17·5 cm) full length pot, and a compost of pure live sphagnum moss. Put two or three large crocks in the bottom to allow rapid drainage of excess water, and fill the pot to within 1 inch (2·5 cm) of the top. The crown should be just on the surface, the rhizome gradually sloping backwards into the moss. Scatter a thin covering of the very finely broken green ends of sphagnum moss which should later become established as a carpet of growing moss. Make a temporary canopy over the pot either with a large bell glass or with a large plastic bag supported by four canes inserted down the sides of the pot. Clip off the corners of the bag to make ventilation holes about $\frac{1}{4}$ inch (6 mm) wide. Now place the pot in a saucer of water in a light part of the cool or cold greenhouse, but entirely shaded from the sun. Under the canopy humidity will be high, and this assists the plant in establishing itself. Watch till growth becomes vigorous, and then increase ventilation by doubling the size of the ventilation holes. A week later, remove the bags and the plant should be well established. Now each day gently water the plant from the top of the pot with the rose of the can, increasing this to twice a day as the weather becomes warmer. Not less than $\frac{1}{2}$ pint (300 ml) a time should be used. In hot weather three times a day will not be too much, and this can be combined with light misting. The water should be cool, preferably not exceeding 50°F (10°C) in temperature. (This can easily be contrived by putting a few ice cubes into the can of soft water some time before use. Such a measure will be particularly necessary in summer if you are in the hotter warm temperate regions.) The function of the frequent watering is not only to provide moisture for the plant but to see that this remains absolutely fresh, and to cool the roots, for overheated roots may cause the plant to die. In winter, watering can be cut to once or twice a week. When the plant is thoroughly established it may be exposed permanently to some sun, though lath or wash shading should be used, and it is wise to entirely protect it from the midday sun.

Frequent repotting is not a good thing, and I like to leave my plants in their pots for at least three years, or for as long as they appear comfortable. The sphagnum around the plant can be expected to grow if conditions are right; this is a good sign, and does not hurt the plant, but it may be necessary to slightly press it down from time to time.

In the higher stations of its native habitats this plant experiences winter frost and snow, and it seems probable that it will prove successful when grown out of doors in some climates. Mr Timothy

Heneage of Somerset, England, uses an identical method to the above, except that they stand in a permanent tray of water in cool, partially shady conditions, and that he does not water them from above. The mean maximum and minimum temperature for January in that neighbourhood is 34–44°F, (1·1–6·6°C) and the plants have experienced temperatures down to 12°F (−11°C) without loss out of doors.

Propagation The best method is by potting up offshoots from the rhizome when these have grown to about a quarter full size. Seed may also be used. Wet these well first by soaking in a jar of water. Shake gently every day, and when they have all sunk sow them as recommended for *Sarracenia*. Try to keep as cool as possible. After they have developed their tiny pitcher leaves water from above gently with a rose daily to several times a day, the object being to keep the roots cool, which are so shallow that they are far more subject to becoming fatally heated than those of the mature plant. When a year old, pot in well broken live sphagnum, using 3 inch (7·5 cm) pots. Mortality is likely to be fairly high, and seed is less satisfactory where small numbers are required than is the offset method.

Flowers of the Cobra Lily *Darlingtonia californica*

The Tropical Pitcher Plant

Until very recently *Nepenthes* were looked upon as subjects for high temperatures and high heating bills in the stovehouse. This is now known to be not necessarily the case. Though best looked upon as stove plants, they can be grown in the warm greenhouse, but growth will be much slower, and the need for frequent syringing or misting makes it impossible to grow many other plants (e.g. the sticky-leaved carnivores) in the same conditions. Nevertheless, so fascinating are the traps in their structure, variety and striking colour variations that a small house devoted entirely to them and perhaps the South American *Utricularias* can provide endless interest. Failing this, you can grow some in a closed tall frame in the warmhouse, while many are suitable for cultivation in the larger terrarium. Mr Joseph Mazrimas finds that most species and hybrids will tolerate a temperature as low as 45–50°F (7·2–10°C) at night, providing the day temperatures are in the eighties Fahrenheit (upper twenties Centigrade). This would give considerable fuel economy during the winter in colder climates. *N. khasiana* is hardier than most, and Mr Joseph P. Contasano of Long Island reports that his plants have survived unintentional winter minimums of between 35 and 40°F (1·6° and 4·4°C) without hurt, though his average daytime temperature at that time is 70°F (21°C). I grew this same species for some years in an unheated propagating frame in a cool greenhouse winter night minimum 40°F (4·4°C)—but without high daytime and higher summertime temperatures growth is extremely slow.

General cultivation Use a 6 inch (16 cm) full length pot for all fully rooted cuttings, and for grown-on seedlings which have formed 1–2 inch (2·5–5 cm) stems. When plants are 3 feet or more (a metre) high transfer to an 8–10 inch (20–28 cm) pot. Alternatively, orchid baskets may be used of the same approximate size.

A variety of compost materials have been used successfully, the most vital quality being that they should remain open and well drained. Equal parts broken sphagnum moss and orchid bark is good, while pure orchid bark has been used satisfactorily. Pure live sphagnum is also much used, but should never be over-compacted or it can become soggy, leading sometimes to rotten roots. Where hard water is used for watering, use a medium of pure inert vermiculite. Three or four medium to large crocks should be placed in the bottom of the pot for drainage. While the plant should be securely planted, the roots do not like to be over-firmed. It is a good plan to sprinkle the surface afterwards with finely broken green live sphagnum moss. In the right conditions this will grow, and though attractive in itself is useful as a guide that all is well. If the pot is too dry this moss will lose its fresh green colour and become lighter, even becoming white if very dry.

Water from the top only; never use a tray. Always keep the compost wet, but as good drainage is essential the container should be placed on a surface that allows the free run-off of excess water, such as slatted open staging or an upturned clay pot. Alternatively, it may be suspended by wire. Use water which is not less than 60°F (15·5°C) in temperature, and it is a good plan to leave a full can permanently in the greenhouse. *Nepenthes* are unusual amongst carnivorous plants in not appearing to be adversely affected by the use of hard water, although this leads to the rapid decay of sphagnum moss and peat, and should only be used when the plants are potted in pure vermiculite.

A high level of humidity, from 70–90 per cent, should be maintained at all times; especially important when temperatures are at their highest. A humidity gauge is useful, though with a little experience it is not difficult to sense the right level. Damp-down the path periodically as required, and at the same time syringe into the air, and lightly mist the foliage till it is wet. These operations should be performed several times a day whenever possible during high temperatures in summer, while in winter once or twice a day will suffice. For those who are away from home during the day this can present difficulties, in which case it is advisable to install an automatically controlled overhead misting system. Mr J. P. Contasano has used such a method over a number of years, and in the permanently damp and highly humid conditions it creates his plants grow extremely well. Hard water, while it does not harm the plants, causes an unattractive deposit to form on the leaves, and eventually clogs the jets. Mr Timothy Heneage has overcome the problem by installing a large rainwater tank below the staging, to which water is piped from the greenhouse guttering. Instead of turning on the water mains, the automatic switch device is connected to an electric pump which takes water from the tank to the jets. When choosing such a pump you must find out the water pressure required from the manufacturers of the misting system.

It was once thought that *Nepenthes* needed to be grown in full shade. While they will grow very well without sun, this often causes them to produce few if any pitchers, and it is therefore important that some sunlight should be provided, but shading is necessary. About 40 per cent natural sunlight, achieved by the use of slatted or wash shading, is best for the majority, though *N. rafflesiana* is better with about 25 per cent. As a general rule the less ventilation the better, and if you can manage to have none at all, so much the better. Excessively high temperatures in summer sun will be minimized by damping-down and adequate shading, but when the temperature rises above 100°F (37·7°C) some ventilation should be given, at the same time damping-down, as the exchange of air would otherwise drastically reduce humidity.

When the first pitchers start to form it is time to start feeding the plants. Six-weekly liquid feeds are then given until autumn. Most proprietary brands are probably suitable, but I prefer an organic type, such as Bio.

Older plants are improved by pruning, as this encourages the production of vigorous healthy young growth, which tends to produce more pitchers. This is usually best done in February or March. The old stems should be cut back as far as possible while still leaving some young growth on the plant. Some of the removed growth will provide useful material for cuttings.

Propagation Cuttings can be taken in spring, summer and autumn, but February or March is usually the best time, for it allows the stock plant time to recover and form pitchers, and it can also coincide with any pruning which may be necessary. The cuttings should be 6–8 inches (15–20 cm) long. One can be taken from the growing end of the shoot, but it is also possible to divide the green stem for some distance beneath into cuttings, each being severed with a diagonal cut a little below the base of a petiole. On the end cutting retain the uppermost fully-grown leaf, removing any which may be beneath. Cuttings taken from the stem beneath this should also each retain an upper leaf only, and the leaves themselves should be shortened by cutting off a third. To prevent the possibility of rot setting in, Mr J. Mazrimas advises putting the whole cutting into a solution of Benomyl or Benlate systemic fungicide for a minute or two. Dipping it into a suitable hormone rooting powder will encourage fast rooting. The cuttings may then be inserted into pots of live sphagnum moss, about half of the stem being buried. The medium should be rather open and not too compacted. These are then lightly watered and placed in a closed propagating case with a bottom heat of at least 70°F (21°C); preferably

Nepenthes ventricosa produces pitchers liberally, and is an accommodating plant for both the stovehouse and heated terrarium.

80°F (26·6°C). Maximum humidity should be maintained, and the cuttings should be frequently dampened with a fine sprayer, though the pots must not be over-watered. In the absence of a propagator with bottom heat, three or four bamboo stakes may be inserted at the sides of the pot to support a polythene bag secured to it with a rubber band, or a suitably-sized propagating dome or bell jar may be placed over the pot, the whole being then placed on a suitably heated surface. Rooting is likely to occur in about four weeks time, but it may be several months before the young plant is sufficiently established for potting-on.

If the seeds are viable—and those of many species are short-lived—most germinate easily, the most important requirement being bottom heat. A suitable compost consists of equal parts of finely broken sphagnum, sand and moss peat. The best container is a seed pan or dwarf pot of suitable size. The seed is sown on the surface and left uncovered. The container is then put in 1 inch (2·5 cm) of water till the surface is moist, and the whole is then placed in a closed propagating case with a bottom heat of 80°F (26·6°C). A high humidity is maintained, and the container should be resoaked if the compost shows signs of becoming dry. Germination usually occurs in from four to six weeks. When large enough to handle, prick out six in a 5 inch (13 cm) dwarf pot, transferring to 6 inch (15 cm) pots when the leaves crowd together.

Terrariums The majority of species will soon outgrow even large terrariums, and it will be necessary to drastically prune them or take fresh cuttings. *N. gracilis*, *N. gracillima* and *N. kampotiana* are less vigorous growers and are suitable for such culture.

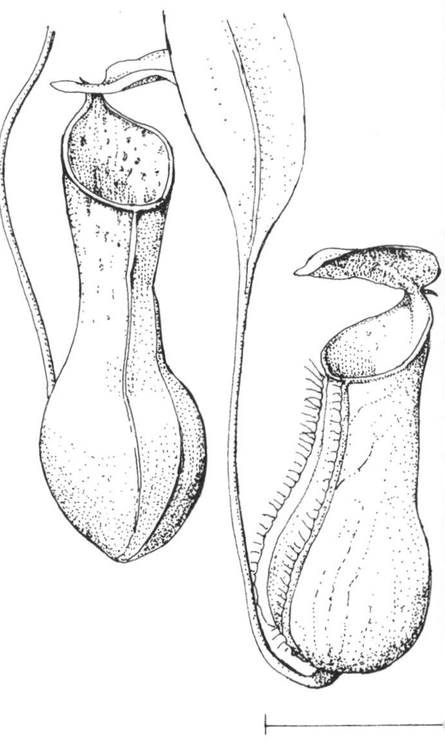

Nepenthes gracilis: upper pitcher on the left, lower pitcher on the right.

The West Australian Pitcher Plant

Cephalotus follicularis

General cultivation A 6 inch (15 cm) full length pot will accommodate one plant, or a 7 inch (17·5 cm) dwarf pot will take three. I prefer clay pots for this species. Compost should be two parts moss peat, two parts good quality oak or beech leaf mould with coarse material sieved off, one part perlite, one part sand. This plant is unusual amongst carnivorous plants in appreciating leaf mould, but its use is not essential, and if not available its place can be taken by more peat. Watering: The pot may be placed in the water tray in summer, but in autumn, winter and spring excessive moisture easily leads to rot. The pot must not stand in water during these seasons, and should be watered only from the top, avoiding the crown of the plant, and maintaining a just damp, rather than wet compost.

In summer the plant prefers shade from midday sun, or light shading on the glass, but to develop bright pitcher coloration it should be given direct sunlight when this is not too strong. It can be kept in the sun for the other seasons. Cool greenhouse.

Comments Most failures with this species seem to be due to keeping the compost too wet, using an unsuitable mixture or too shallow containers. The plant has long roots, and larger pots mean larger plants. Be sure to remove dead leaves and pitchers and do not wet the foliage or crown in winter.

Cephalotus follicularis pitcher

Propagation In time these plants form clumps which may readily be divided. An alternative method is by thick root cuttings taken from a large plant in April or May. The root cutting should be $\frac{1}{2}$–1 inch (1·3–2·5 cm) long, cleanly cut with a sharp knife. Use a 5 inch (13 cm) dwarf pot and a compost of two parts sand to one of moss peat. Lay the cuttings flat, and cover with $\frac{1}{8}$ inch (3 mm) of compost. Water by tray. As soon as several leaves have been produced, pot as for parent plant. Another method is to take leaf cuttings. Remove entire leaves, or pitchers with the entire stalk attached, and insert the base of the leaf or stalk by up to a $\frac{1}{4}$ inch (6 mm) into a bed of live sphagnum. Do not cover the blade or pitcher itself with moss, but otherwise use the same method and equipment recommended for *Drosera* leaf cuttings (page 214).

The Rainbow Plant

Byblis liniflora is an annual species which, if it is to flower, should be raised early from seed. It is best in the warm greenhouse.

General cultivation Sow the seeds in February in seed pans or dwarf pots, scattering them sparsely over the levelled surface of a compost consisting of two parts of sand to one of moss peat. Alternatively, you may use pure shredded living sphagnum moss. Do not bury them. Soak container in 1 inch (2·5 cm) of water till the surface appears moist, drain, and keep the plant in a light place, preferably in a temperature of 70–75°F (21–23·8°C): various electrically heated propagators will provide such conditions. Do not let it dry out, but the compost should be only just moist and never soggy. In this temperature germination should take about four weeks. If grown in the propagator they should now be slowly hardened off, daily increasing ventilation by gradually raising the ventilator top at one end with a wedge, before moving them to the lower temperature of the warm greenhouse. When the seedlings are $\frac{3}{4}$–1 inch (2–2·5 cm) high they should be transplanted to their permanent quarters. Use a 4 inch (10 cm) full length plastic pot, with a compost of equal parts moss peat, perlite and sand, or sand and moss peat in equal proportions. Keep in a saucer, putting in sufficient water to be easily sucked up by the pot to maintain a constantly moist but not soaking compost. Place it in a sunny position, close to the glass of the warm greenhouse. It can also be grown in a lighted and heated terrarium, but needs very good light.

pp. 97, 98 *B. gigantea* This is a definite perennial and a rather easier plant than the above.

General cultivation Use a 6 inch (15 cm) full length pot, same compost as for *B. liniflora*. Mound this a little towards the centre. Watering and position as for *B. liniflora*. Cool greenhouse. Old yellowing stems may be removed from near the base when young growth is present which will replace them.

Propagate by seed or root cuttings. Seed is poor-germinating unless exposed to fire, and the plant apparently depends much upon natural bush fires in nature. I sow mine in the coolhouse in April or May. Prepare a fire-proof seed pan or dwarf pot (ordinary terracotta clay) and sow and moisten as for *B. liniflora*. When the surface is moist, drain, and pile a cone of dry hay or crushed tissue paper over this. Ignite it so that it burns fiercely, and when it is cold remove what ashes you can. Germination should follow in four to six weeks time. The plants should be flowering by the following spring. Cultivated plants do not normally produce seed, unless hand pollinated, but the anthers will not release their pollen unless vibrated. In nature this is accomplished by a small bumble bee or by the wind,[17] but in cultivation this vibration must be artificially produced by hand on a hot day after several hours of sunshine, the pollen then being transferred to the stigma of another flower.

Root cuttings provide a rather less reliable method of raising stock, as they are inclined to rot. Take them in April or May from a well established plant, with a sharp knife cleanly cutting them into lengths of 1 inch (2·5 cm) to $1\frac{1}{2}$ inch (3·5 cm) long. A 5 inch (13 cm) dwarf pot is suitable. Use a compost of two parts sand to one of moss peat, laying them flat and even, covering with about an $\frac{1}{8}$ inch (3 mm) of the same compost. Keep moist but not wet.

The Portuguese Sundew

Many still regard *Drosophyllum lusitanicum* as a difficult plant to successfully cultivate, while the majority of those who do succeed appear to lose their plant immediately it produces seed. A mistaken belief has thus come about that it is biennial—quite belied by the ancient shrublets to be found in its natural habitats. The truth is that it is an easy plant to grow to a respectable old age once a method is adopted which overcomes its several hatreds. These are a wet collar, overwatering (especially in winter), misting or spraying of the foliage, poor drainage, poor light, and—most of all—root disturbance. I was at first quite unsuccessful, but after initial trials and errors I eventually concluded that even if transplated with every care as a small seedling the shock of the disturbance appeared to inhibit the development of the root system, which in old and healthy plants is extensive. Such plants were unlikely to survive for more than a year at the utmost, and in this may be the origin of the biennial idea! My method is as follows.

pp. 99, 101

General cultivation Sow in spring so that the plants have developed woody stems by autumn. All pots *must* be of clay, their porosity being vital to the method. Take a $4\frac{1}{2}$ inch (11 cm) full length pot and insert a wick consisting of several long pieces of sphagnum moss through its drainage hole. Put a large drainage crock over the latter, and make sure the wick protrudes to the side of this, and also through the bottom of the pot (see diagram). Now cover the crock with a thin layer of sphagnum. Fill the pot to within $\frac{1}{4}$ inch (6 mm) of the top with a compost of two parts granulated moss peat, two parts John Innes Potting Compost No. 2, and one and a half parts of sand, gently firming this. Sow two or three seeds in the central part, $\frac{1}{8}$ inch (3 mm) deep and $\frac{3}{4}$ inch (2 cm) apart. Gently firm. Place in $1\frac{1}{2}$ inches (3·5 cm) of water till the surface is damp. Allow to drain. Place a sheet of glass over the top of the pot to cut down evaporation, placing a piece of card or paper over this to cut out all light. I never apply bottom heat, finding the

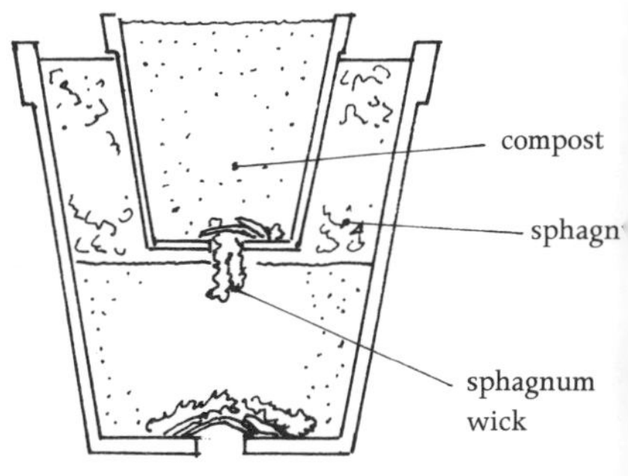

The arrangement of pots for cultivating *Drosphyllum lusitanicum*

coolhouse temperature adequate for germination within about six weeks time. Regularly inspect the pot. If the compost is becoming dry it should be watered using the immersion technique as above—you must not water from the top. At the first sign of germination the glass is removed. The plant is now placed in a sunny position close to the glass of the greenhouse.

Extreme care is needed in watering; it is not a bog plant and will soon die if overwatered, but will be equally sure to do so if the roots are allowed to become dry. *Always* water by immersion, and *always* do so if you are going out for the day and there is the slightest chance of its drying out; these first months are crucial. If more than one seed germinates, pull out the unwanted ones, making quite sure you do not disturb your selected seedling.

When the plant has formed its sixth leaf you can proceed with the next stage. Select a 7 or 8 inch (17·5 or 20 cm) clay pot, place three or four crocks over the drainage hole, and just cover these with sphagnum moss. Sufficient of the recommended compost is added and firmed, so that if the 4½ inch (11 cm) pot is placed on it, its rim is at least ½ inch (1·3 cm) above that of the larger. Now put an even layer of sphagnum moss over the compost, using sufficient to ensure that when the smaller pot is placed firmly over it its rim is now ¾ inch (2 cm) proud of that of the larger pot. Hold it there, and pack the space between the two pots firmly to within ⅓ inch (8 mm) of the rim of the larger pot. Now water this sphagnum moss well, and place the pot again in a sunny position near the glass.

The sphagnum moss acts as a reservoir which allows only sufficient water to percolate through the clay sides of the smaller pot, leaving the raised part of the pot, and with it the base of the plant's stem, relatively dry. Normally one waters *only* via the sphagnum, without wetting the surface of the compost. However, during hot summer weather when the plant is over a year old I find it does no harm to apply water to both pots, though I would never do this in cool weather or in any other season. One needs to be especially careful not to overwater the moss during the period after flowering while the seed is developing; at this time growth is minimal and the constitution of the plant is at its most delicate. Always water when the moss feels dryish but not crisp to the touch. If the roots are allowed to dry out only once the plant is almost certain to die.

Species cultivation

The Butterworts

All the *Pinguiculas* hate root disturbance, and should never be repotted while in summer growth. This will almost certainly result in the death of many, particularly the species forming winter resting buds.

Species forming winter resting buds

The following three species should be grown in cool conditions. The normal cool greenhouse conditions prevent them from making satisfactory winter resting buds, and without these they will seldom if ever survive more than a couple of years. They should therefore be grown in pots in the open air, preferably in a good light, but entirely shaded from the sun through at least the middle hours of the day. Humidity is important, so water on the tray system. Keep them far away from hot, sunny places such as the vicinity of a stone sun terrace or the sunny walls of the house, as this might result in hot and dry air affecting the plants. My plants are within an area of largely dappled shade cast by several trees, which help to create an ideal microclimate. Even so, I am dubious as to whether those who live in warmer temperate regions could expect much luck with *Pinguicula alpina* under anything but laboratory-created conditions, though I would expect them to succeed with the easy and very beautiful *P. grandiflora*.

The pots must be protected from birds, many of which will root about after grubs in the pots, especially in winter, so these should either be placed in a fruit cage, under netting, or in a cold frame which should at all times be well aired.

All three species are easily raised from seed, which should be fresh. I prefer to sow mine in December or January, the crucial thing being that there should be frosts ahead, as all, particularly *P. alpina*, benefit from frost stratification. Sow in a seed pan or 4 inch (10 cm) dwarf pot, in a compost of equal quantities peat and sand. Level the surface, scatter seed sparsely and do not bury. Stand container permanently in a tray or saucer of soft water under a well-aired frame. Expose the seed to as many frosts as possible, and to ensure this, it is a good idea actually to stand the pots in the open during two or three frosty nights. Sufficient frosting should ensure that a very high proportion of the seed germinates in the spring; however, it often happens that none does. In this case, providing the seed was fresh and viable, you may be disappointed but need not be unduly concerned. Wait another year, keeping the pot standing in water and free of weed, and allowing several frosts to penetrate again during the following winter, and a high germination usually results the following spring. When large enough to handle, the seedlings may be pricked out into their permanent growing positions in pots, using the same growing methods as for mature plants. Most will reach semi-maturity before they die down to their winter hibernacula.

Species cultivation

The Irish Butterwort *Pinguicula grandiflora*

Never transplant when in growth. Do this between autumn and spring when in the hibernaculum stage and therefore rootless. The hibernaculum should be only half buried: if fully buried it will die.

P. vulgaris A 5 inch (13 cm) dwarf pot allows room for three plants. To prevent restriction of the leaves, fill the pot to the brim with a compost of two parts moss peat to one of sand. The most convenient method of propagation is to remove gemmae from around the parent hibernaculum in spring, just before the roots form. The gemmae are, in effect, miniature hibernacula, and are cultivated in the same way. Also by seed (see above).

P. grandiflora and *P. grandiflora* ssp. *rosea* A 5 inch (13 cm) dwarf pot will hold three plants. Use a compost of four parts moss peat, two parts John Innes Potting Compost No. 2, one part sand, filling the pot to the brim, mounding it slightly to the centre and embedding several stones in the surface, between which hibernacula are planted. This species is so generous in its production of gemmae that the use of seed is pointless if you already have stock—treat in same way as adult plants.

p. 113 *P. alpina* Use a 4 or 5 inch (10 or 13 cm) dwarf pot, and a compost of one part John Innes No. 2 compost, two parts sand, three parts moss peat. Mound up surface and embed stones exactly as for *P. grandiflora*. *P. alpina* hates root disturbance at all times, for the hibernaculum retains its roots, so always raise from seed, keeping the plants permanently in the pots to which you transplanted the seedlings.

Species not forming winter resting buds

Much difficulty has been experienced in growing many of these species for any length of time.

P. hirtiflora I grow and propagate this species as I do *P. caudata* and *P. mexicana* (see below). An easy and worthwhile plant.

p. 114 *P. lutea* I have failed to keep this species for more than a year under coolhouse conditions, but seem to be experiencing some success outside where it is protected from strong sunlight in the middle hours of the day. A 5 inch (13 cm) dwarf pot accommodates three plants, and the compost is two parts sand to one of moss peat. Watering: tray. In winter the plants are placed in a well-aired frame, the compost being kept only just damp. Propagation is by seed. I have not tried leaf cuttings from this species but several friends have had success with these.

P. planifolia and *P. caerulea* I cannot claim long success with either species, but the former seems to be responding to the method used for *P. lutea*, which I shall also try for *P. caerulea*. Again, it is too early to report definite success.

Species cultivation

P. primuliflora Use a 6 inch (15 cm) dwarf pot and a compost of two parts sand to one of moss peat. Watering: tray in summer, but keep compost only on the damp side in winter. Position: lightly shaded. Propagation by plantlets which arise from the ends of older leaves, or by leaf cuttings (see below).

P. lusitanica A small plastic seed tray or shallow seed pan is preferable to a dwarf pot. The compost is equal parts peat and sand or shredded long-fibre sphagnum moss. The plant should be in a semi-shaded but light place in the cool greenhouse, or in mid-temperate regions they may be grown in a shaded airy frame. It likes high humidity, and a propagator cover is an advantage, even when grown out of doors. A good plant for a humid terrarium, if placed within 12 inches (30 cm) of a light tube. Keep damp but not soggy, especially in winter. Propagation by seed.

p. 115

P. caudata, P. mexicana and probably any others of the *P. moranensis* type. A 5 inch (13 cm) dwarf pot per plant, with a compost of four parts moss peat, two parts John Innes Compost No. 2, one part sand. Watering: tray. They prefer a sunny place, lightly shaded in a cool or warm greenhouse, though they will flower in light but sunless places. Also very good as a houseplant in a light place in window or under fluorescent light. Propagation is by division when in winter rosette, or leaf cuttings (see below).

p. 106, 108–9

P. gypsicola One plant to a 4 inch (10 cm) dwarf pot, or three to a 5 inch (13 cm) dwarf pot, in the same compost as for *P. caudata*. Watering: tray during growing period, but not in winter, when it becomes almost dormant and could be subject to attack from Botrytis mould. To avoid this possibility, I keep the compost almost completely dry during this period, gradually resuming watering in the spring. Position: as for *P. caudata* in cool or warm greenhouse. Propagation is by leaf cuttings.

p. 117

Leaf cuttings This vegetative method of propagation is mainly used for species of the heterophyllous growth type. I prefer to use only the thick succulent leaves peculiar to the winter rosette. In the case of *P. caudata* and *P. mexicana* I take these in spring, just as the first summer leaves are to be seen emerging from the centre of the rosette. The plant is gently lifted, and as much soil as possible washed from its roots. Not more than half the leaves are then removed, starting from the outermost leaves and rotating round the plant. Each should be cleanly broken off by a downward pull, so as to include as much of the narrow stalk-like base as possible, and be put aside for about twenty minutes so that the break may seal. A similar propagator to that recommended for *Drosera* leaf cuttings should be used (see page 214), but I prefer to use a compost of sand and peat in equal proportions rather than live sphagnum, for the cuttings are likely to be swamped by the growth of the moss. Make the compost level, and place the leaves on the surface, making sure that each is the right way up. The broken end of the stalk should be in full contact with the compost, although no part of the upper part of the blade should be covered, and by making a dent in the compost with a finger at a slightly inclined angle it is simple to create a comfortable bed for the leaf in which the base is in full contact.

After you have arranged your cuttings, place the box in an inch (2·5 cm) of water, and when the surface is just damp remove it to drain well on some staging, then place it in a sunless part of the cool or warm greenhouse and cover with the propagator lid, allowing a little top ventilation. Shake off the condensation drops daily which form on the lid and may otherwise drop on to the cuttings. At the same time remove any rotting leaves. In about four weeks some of the leaves will be seen to have one to several tiny buds around their bases. By August the propagator cover can be entirely removed to allow the plantlets to adapt to your normal greenhouse humidity, but they are not normally ready for potting till spring or early summer the following year. Keep them just damp rather than wet in winter.

P. gypsicola is treated in precisely the same way, and the cuttings are taken at the same time, even though the summer foliage may have shown no signs of developing. *P. hirtiflora* leaf cuttings are also treated similarly. I prefer to use the outer leaves only, taking these from the plant in mid-May.

The Sundews

General cultivation The different species of *Drosera* differ in their requirements as far as light is concerned. Most, with some notable exceptions, are sun-lovers, but they do not like to be roasted, and where a sunny aspect is advised, 50 per cent lath shading is advisable in sunny warm-temperate climates, while in most northern temperate regions little if any shading is normally required. Most will also do well in terrariums if placed about 12 inches (30 cm) below the fluorescent lights.

The tray system of watering (see page 187) is suitable for most and it is essential that the water be soft. The trays should be empty of water in the winter months, but except where otherwise stated, the compost should be moist.

Sundews are subject to very few pests and diseases. Aphids may affect the flowering stalks and unopened leaves, but are usually few and can be conveniently removed by hand. My own technique is to use an ordinary water-colour brush dipped in the mucilage secretion from one of the larger sundews. If infestation is wide, use BHC smoke as recommended by the manufacturers. The grey Botrytis mould may sometimes affect and kill the crowns of rosette-forming *Droseras* in winter. This disease is encouraged by excessively high humidity often combined with poor light and low temperatures. Dead rosettes should be cut off at their base, removed and burnt, when new growth may spring from the unaffected roots by early summer. If infection is widespread, monthly spraying through the remaining winter months with the systemic fungicide Benlate may be justified. This makes the plants look temporarily unhealthy, mucilage often ceasing to be produced for a time, and it kills live sphagnum moss, but it is an effective control.

Propagation Propagation is usually best by seed or leaf cuttings and occasionally by root cuttings. Seed should be sown sparsely on the surface of the same compost as is recommended for the parent plant. Except where stated it is wise to sow in spring or early summer, so that a strong plant is produced by autumn. Germination may take from five to many weeks. Prick out into pans, boxes or into their permanent pot when large enough to handle, digging up carefully so as not to injure the roots. Not all species germinate easily, but where they do it is the best means of obtaining large numbers of plants, even though these take considerably longer to mature than do cuttings.

Leaf cuttings often provide the best means of obtaining large plants in a relatively short time, and are best taken in late spring or early summer, which usually allows time for the plants to reach semi-maturity by the autumn. Humidity is important, and I use either a seed box complete with clear polystyrene propagator cover, or place the box within a large propagator (see p. 194). For a minimum quantity, a 5 inch (13 cm) pot with propagating dome is sufficient. Fill the box with live broken sphagnum moss, wet the surface only with water from the fine rose of a can and gently firm. Then use a flat piece of wood or something similar to press as level a surface as possible a $\frac{1}{2}$–$\frac{1}{4}$ inch (1·3 cm–6 mm) below the top of the box. For your cuttings, select only healthy leaves which should be young, but completely opened with fully bedewed tentacles. Leaf forms provide some guide as to the best type of cut. With the *D. binata* complex it is best to remove the blade together with $\frac{1}{8}$ inch (3 mm) of the petiole, as is also the case with the very different leaf of *D. capensis*. In the case of *D. anglica, D. intermedia* and *D. rotundifolia* I take the blade with the best part of the petiole attached, while the leaves of *D. filiformis* may be cut into lengths between $\frac{1}{2}$ and 1 inch (1·3 and 2·5 cm) long. With leaves of the *D. spathulata* type, and in *D. adelae* and *D. schizandra*, it is advisable to cut as near the base of the whole leaf as possible. When in doubt, the blade with a small part of the petiole attached should suffice. A small sharp scalpel will be found handy to ensure a clean cut, or failing that, a razor blade.

Lay the leaves, tentacle side uppermost, flat on the sphagnum surface. It is very important that they remain entirely flat and in contact with it, and those which do not may be held down with the aid of a minimum of small pebbles or crocks. Now select a few green, growing ends of some pieces of live sphagnum, gently squeezing the water out of them, and break these up into minute pieces. Use this mash to almost completely cover the leaf blades in the *thinnest possible* layer, allowing glimpses through to the leaf blade here and there. Then gently press this covering with your forefinger into full contact with the leaf. Now put the box in a shallow water tray till it has absorbed its fill, allow to drain, cover with the lid, and place the propagator in the cool greenhouse or in the window of a warm room. If the lid has adjustable ventilators, these should be a quarter open. It should be in a light place, but must be completely shaded from the direct sun.

In about four weeks buds will start to form at the base of tentacles on some or all of the leaves, but it may not be for several weeks more that growth will be seen above the moss. When small healthy plants have formed, the lid may be removed and the plants gradually introduced to lightly shaded sunlight. The more vigorous species may often be allowed to grow on in the tray for several months before potting up, but others should be potted sooner if there is a risk of this becoming smothered by the growing sphagnum.

With skill resulting from experience your rate of success is likely to increase, and you may then try cutting the blades into smaller segments, when a greater increase per leaf may often be expected.

Some sundews produce thick roots which are suitable as material for root cuttings, examples being *D. hamiltonii*, *D. aliciae*, *D. capensis* and the *D. binata* complex. A large well-established plant is unpotted and one or two of the stoutest roots removed. These are then cut into lengths between $\frac{1}{4}$ and $\frac{1}{2}$ inch (6mm and 1·3 cm) long. These may be then treated in exactly the same way as that described for leaf cuttings, with the exception that the roots should be wholly covered with the moss, and that better results are obtained if the propagator is placed in a temperature of around 70°F (21°C). It usually takes longer to obtain mature plants this way than with leaf cuttings, but its chief disadvantage is it means disturbing the root systems of good plants.

Species forming winter buds

These are not satisfactory plants for the greenhouse, for in such conditions they do not form adequate hibernacula and often fail to survive the winter. They should be grown out of doors in the summer, the pots standing in trays of soft water. Birds love to root about in the pots, and it is wise to protect them with a net canopy or fruit-cage. All appreciate full sun in most temperate climates, but in the hottest warm-temperate regions shading from the hot midday sun may be necessary.

p. 120 *D. rotundifolia* Use a compost of finely broken pure sphagnum moss, preferably live, in a shallow seed pan, plastic seed box or dwarf pot from 3 inches (7·5 cm) upwards. Position: sunny. Propagate by seed scattered on the surface of the same compost and container as for adult plants, or by leaf cuttings.

D. anglica As for *D. rotundifolia*, but use a dwarf pot of not less than 5 inches (13 cm) diameter. p. 129

D. filiformis var. *filiformis* As for *D. rotundifolia*, but use full length 4 inch (10 cm) pot. p. 131

D. filiformis var. *tracyi* As for *D. rotundifolia*, but use full length 5 inch (13 cm) pot. In colder parts of north temperate climates this plant may need protection from severe frost.

D. intermedia Use a pure granulated moss peat compost, well wetted before use, in a shallow 5 inch (13 cm) seed pan or half-sized plastic seed tray. The water level should at first be level with the surface of the peat, but when the plants are established and in full growth this should cover its surface by up to $\frac{1}{8}$ inch (3 mm), for these plants grow best as semi-aquatics. Position: sunny. Propagation by seed and division.

D. linearis The compost should be granulated moss peat mixed with a third sand, in a 4 inch (10 cm) dwarf pot. Position: sunny. Propagation: seed.

Drosera hybrids. Treat *D.* x *obovata* (*D. anglica* x *D. rotundifolia* as for *D. anglica*, except that it is sterile, so must be propagated from leaf cuttings or divisions only, while *D.* x 'Californica' (*D. filiformis filiformis* x *D. filiformis tracyi*) should be cultivated as for *D. filiformis tracyi*.

Other rosette-forming sundews

D. spathulata complex. There are a number of plants of rather different appearance at present considered as varieties or forms of *D. spathulata*, all of which require similar treatment. Compost: two thirds peat, one third sand, in a 4–5 inch (10–13 cm) dwarf pot. Watering: tray. Position: sunny, in a cool greenhouse. Propagation by seed and leaf cuttings. p. 132

D. montana This pretty species was excluded from the main text due to its similarity to a small *D. spathulata* 'Kanto'. The tentacles are vivid red, and the small flowers are white. Treatment and propagation as for *D. spathulata*.

D. brevifolia A tiny red-leaved blush-flowered sundew from North America. Treat and propagate as for *D. montana*. Short-lived perennial.

The English Sundew *Drosera anglica*. Two embryo leafblades can be seen, as well as a coiled flower stalk bearing flower buds.

Drosera cistiflora, mainly a winter grower, dying back to the root in summer, when the pot should be dried out. Recommence watering in late autumn. See also p. 136.

Species cultivation

D. burmanii Use a compost of two thirds peat, one third sand or, where available, pure long-fibre sphagnum, in a 4 inch (10 cm) full sized pot. Watering: tray. Cool or (better) warm greenhouse, sunny position. This species is short lived, and best treated as an annual. Propagation by seed only.

D. capillaris A compost of equal parts peat and sand, or pure long-fibre sphagnum, in a 4 inch (10 cm) dwarf pot. Watering: tray. Position: sunny, in a cool greenhouse. This is also short lived, so ensure against loss by collecting seed. Propagation is by seed and leaf cuttings.

South African sundews

D. cuneifolia Compost is long-fibre or live sphagnum moss, in a 5 inch (13 cm) full sized pot (the depth is important for roots). Watering: tray. Cool greenhouse, sunny. Propagation: seed and leaf cuttings.

D. trinervia Treat and propagate as *D. cuneifolia.*

D. aliciae Treat as *D. cuneifolia,* but I find a compost of two thirds peat to one of sand satisfactory.

D. natalensis Use a compost of either pure sphagnum (long-fibre or live), or two thirds peat and one third sand, in a 5 inch (13 cm) full sized pot. Keep moist but do *not* stand continuously in water. Sunny position in a cool greenhouse. Propagation is by seed and leaf cuttings.

D. capensis Treat and propagate as *D. aliciae*. A 4 inch (10 cm) pot is large enough for the smaller narrow-leaf form.

D. regia Use a compost of three parts peat to one of sand in a 13 cm full sized pot. Shade from direct sunlight. Propagate from root cuttings.

D. cistiflora The compost is two parts of peat to one part of sand, in a 13 cm full sized pot. Watering when in growth: tray. When plant shows signs of approaching dormancy (die-back of foliage) allow pot to dry out, and keep completely dry during dormant period. When new growth emerges some six months later watering is recommenced by tray method. Propagation by leaf cuttings and seed.

The pygmy sundews

These not only include such fascinating miniatures as *D. pygmaea* but also plants with beautiful flowers so large that they may almost equal the size of the rosette from which they spring. Of the latter, some of the best are of very recent discovery and have yet to be officially named. These are for the moment known by the Australian place names where they were discovered (e.g. sp. 'Bannister'). They possess the same charm that alpine plant enthusiasts know in the Kabschia or Cushion Saxifrages, which, from a distance, they somewhat resemble in flower.

Species cultivation

All take up little space and are well worth trying, and we can now expect a steady increase in the number in cultivation. Most plants not listed below should respond successfully to one or other of the cultural methods given. One I and others have so far had no success with is *D. glanduligera* which, although an easy germinator, has never survived for long.

General cultivation The compost, pot size and watering requirements vary, and are given below. All like a sunny position, yet resent fierce sun. A light position in a cool greenhouse, but with shade from strong sunlight, is advisable—the less shade you can manage to use without harm the better. Propagation is by gemmae, seed if produced, and leaf cuttings. The gemmae are produced by most species in winter, and are best removed with a water-colour brush and scattered over identical compost and given similar treatment to the parent plant. Most grow quickly, usually flowering the same year. Accumulation of gemmae over the plant can lead to its death by smothering, Botrytis mould sometimes setting in, so it is wise to remove these even if you do not require them for propagation. They are easily swept away with the brush if the pot is held on its side.

Drosera scorpioides, an Australian pygmy sundew, here much enlarged. The feathery white structures surrounding the centre of the plant are much-toothed stipules.

Easier species The following may be grown several plants to a 4 inch (10 cm) pot, in a compost of equal parts sand and granulated moss peat; the material I use with excellent results. Pure milled sphagnum is preferred by many, but live sphagnum should never be used. All are best stood in a water tray during the summer, and at all times the compost should be moist and never be allowed to become dry: sp. 'Bannister', sp. 'Beermullah', *dichrosepala*, sp. 'Millbrook Road', *miniata*, sp. 'Moora', sp. 'Muchea Pink', *nitidula*, *platystigma*, *pulchella*, *scorpioides*, sp. 'Toodyay Pink'.

Difficult species *D. androsacea* and *D. leucoblasta* are best grown in pure milled sphagnum (*not* live sphagnum), but where this is not available a compost of equal parts peat and sand is acceptable. They are deep-rooting, and a 4 or 5 inch (10 or 13 cm) full length pot should be used. The surface of the compost should be slightly mounded towards the centre, so that the crowns of the plants remain dry when watering from above. They normally grow through the winter to spring, becoming dormant in late spring. During growth the compost should be moist, but the plant must not be stood at any time permanently in water. Watering should be by immersion in 2 inches (5 cm) of water, removing to drain on staging when the surface is obviously moist, or by gently watering the side of the surface from above without touching the crowns of the plants. During dormancy, the compost should be dryish without ever being allowed to desiccate, a very little water carefully being applied from above when necessary.

Species cultivation

Tuber-forming species

Most (those listed separately below are exceptions) require the following treatment. If this is followed no difficulties should arise, but if water is applied during dormancy the tuber will almost inevitably rot. Prepare compost of 1 part sand to 2 parts peat and dry this out completely (spread a shallow layer on a metal tray placed on a stove). Store the tuber in a clip-tight polythene packet in a dark place till it starts to produce a shoot, when it must be planted in a 15 cm pot in the specially dried compost. The tuber should be buried to a depth twice that of its own size, but after scooping out the planting hole to this depth it is advisable firstly to *just* cover the shoot with compost, then cover the hole with an inverted cup to cut out the light. Every time the shoot emerges, just cover again with more compost, replacing the cup each time until the hole is filled, when the cup is removed. When the shoot emerges from this final layer the surface of the compost is lightly misted with water from a hand-sprayer, and this is repeated daily. In this way a minute, and gradually increasing moisture content is built up in the compost which still remains apparently dry. When the first leaf commences to unfurl the spraying is discontinued, and the tray system of watering is used. Approaching dormancy is indicated when the leaves start to yellow or die back, and the pot is then removed from the water tray and allowed to dry out (use of a non-porous pot ensures that this is gradual). The compost must be kept completely dry during the entire period of dormancy, but the pot should remain in the greenhouse, for the humidity will prevent partial dehydration of the tuber, which can occur if pot is transferred to too dry an atmosphere.

When the shoot emerges in the second year the spray-followed-by-tray system of watering is followed, as described above. The tuber may normally remain in the same compost and pot for many years; indeed the tuber should be disturbed as little as possible. Sometimes – not always for any apparent reason – a tuber will fail to produce a shoot. In this case keep the compost dry and do not disturb the tuber. Usually it will shoot in the following year, when it is given normal treatment, though I have had cases where this dormancy has lasted two years.

D. hamiltonii Use a compost of two thirds peat, one third leaf mould, in a 5 inch (13 cm) dwarf pot. Watering: tray. Position: half sun, in a cool greenhouse. To induce flowering, expose the plant to winter cold, but avoid the possibility of frosting.

D. gigantea The compost should be equal parts sand and moss peat, in a 5 inch (13 cm) *clay* full length pot. Watering: from about midwinter stand the pot permanently in water. When the plant dies down (some time in summer) gradually withhold water. Let the pot dry out completely, placing it again in the water tray in midwinter. Position: sunny, in a cool greenhouse. Try not to disturb roots, and if for any reason this is necessary, do so immediately after they die down and at no other time, for the delicate stems between the tuber and surface are easily broken. Propagation is by seed sown in autumn, using a 5 inch (13 cm) pot and the same compost mix. I grow *D. peltata*, *D. menziesii* and *D. auriculata* with some success the same way.

North Queensland sundews

D. adelae Compost should be pure live sphagnum moss, slightly broken, in a 5 inch (13 cm) full length pot. Watering: tray. Keep it in a warm greenhouse, as it does not do well in cooler winter conditions, and shade it from direct sun as it hates strong sunlight. It may also be grown in the terrarium under fluorescent lights (sixteen hour photoperiod) or near a window, but it often prospers in a warm humid kitchen window without such protection. Propagation is by leaf cuttings and seed.

D. prolifera Treat as for *D. schizandra*. Offspring generate from the ends of the trailing flowering scapes.

D. schizandra Treat as for *D. adelae* in almost all respects, but it does best if a minimum winter temperature of 50°F (10°C) is maintained. High humidity is important; it grows well in a sunless window indoors when the pot is covered with a propagating dome, and in the terrarium (sixteen hour photoperiod).

Fork-leaved sundews

These often very attractive plants in the *Drosera binata* complex are amongst the easiest to cultivate. They thrive in either a compost of two parts moss peat to one of sand, or in pure live sphagnum moss. Watering: tray. Position: sunny, in a cool greenhouse. Propagation: leaf cuttings are best, and soon mature, but plants may also be produced from root cuttings.

D. binata 'T Form' Use 5 inch (13 cm) dwarf pot. The plant has a period of winter dormancy.

D. binata dichotoma 'Small Type'. Treat as for typical form.

D. binata dichotoma 'Giant Type'. Use 7 inch (17·5 cm) dwarf pot to accommodate its large roots.

D. binata multifida Use 5 inch (13 cm) full length pot. This plant does not die down unless subjected to too much cold.

Drosera binata 'T Form'

D. binata multifida 'Pink Form'. Treat as for 'T Form'.

D. binata multifida 'Extrema'. As above, but also looks very fine when grown in a wire basket filled with live sphagnum, watering from above.

D. x *dinata* (*D. binata dichotoma* x *D. binata* 'T Form'). As for 'T Form'.

Interspecies hybrids

D. x Nagamoto (*D. anglica* x *D. spathulata* 'Kansai Type'). Use a compost of pure live sphagnum moss slightly broken, or two thirds peat to one third sand, in a 5 inch (13 cm) dwarf pot. Watering: tray. Position: sun with light shading, in a cool to warm greenhouse. Try to keep temperature above 42°F (5·5°C), or the plant will die back to a resting bud, when it may rot. If it does die back, it may be safely stored till the spring in the non-freezing compartment of the refrigerator. Propagation: as it is sterile it will not set seed, so propagate from leaf cuttings.

D. x *wateri (D. anglica* x *D. spathulata* 'Kanto Type'). As for D. x 'Nagamoto'.

D. x *hybrida (D. filiformis* x *D. intermedia).* This is hibernaculum-forming, and should be grown out of doors in the same way as *D. filiformis filiformis.*

The Venus Fly Trap

Though *Dionaea muscipula* must be one of the easiest of plants to grow, the failure rate experienced by would-be growers is extremely high. This is sometimes due to the purchase of inferior material, and I would recommend starting with healthy potted plants in a mature state of growth. The so-called dry 'bulbs' are not in fact bulbs at all, but plants from which the leaves have been removed and which all too often have been taken from one of their ever-decreasing natural habitats. Failure is sometimes due to unsuitable compost, and quite as often caused by the use of too small a container, while plants in the house are often deprived of adequate light.

General cultivation Use a 4 or 5 inch (10 or 13 cm) dwarf pot. Plants are sold in smaller pots, and may thrive in these for weeks or even months afterwards, but sooner or later rapid deterioration and almost inevitably root rot set in, so it is best to repot soon after buying. The compost should be moss peat and sand in equal proportions, or where horticultural sand is unobtainable moss peat alone has been found satisfactory. Avoid like the plague perlite, sphagnum moss, or indeed any alternative compost. Watering: tray. It likes a sunny place, when the inner surfaces of the traps often colour brilliantly, but it will grow in sunless places in a good light. The cool greenhouse is suitable, or a window sill, where the pot should stand in a wide saucer of water to create adequate humidity. Young flowering scapes are best removed as soon as they appear unless seed is required, as flowering has a decidedly weakening effect upon the plant.

Propagation Seeds should be sparsely scattered over the compost in a 4 or 5 inch (10 or 13 cm) pot, and only just covered with a scattering of fine dry moss peat through a fine-mesh kitchen sieve. Then gently spray this surface till moist and place the pot in a water tray. Plants usually take from five to seven years to reach flowering size under normal conditions.

Leaf cuttings are best taken in late spring or early summer. The leaf should be young and healthy, though mature. The whole plant should be lifted so that the entire leaf together with its base may be removed. This is then treated in exactly the same way as a *Drosera* leaf cutting (see page 214), with the exception that one need not bother to break up the thin covering layer of green sphagnum quite so finely, and it is usually impractical to cover much of the trap itself. After the first few days they should be examined, as movement of the traps often causes the cuttings to shift, in which case the wide blade-like petiole may need to be re-anchored. They usually take up to ten weeks to form buds, but may take much longer. When large enough to handle, transplant to the recommended compost. If bottom heat can be provided—70–80°F (21–26·6°C)—this helps to speed the process, and may result in a higher strike percentage. Leaves often start to die from the ends, but this is unimportant unless grey mould (*Botrytis cinerea*) sets in, in which case that part of the leaf should be removed. Fleshy leaf bases from the 'bulb' may also be used to make leaf cuttings using the same method.

The Waterwheel plant

p. 161 *Aldrovanda vesiculosa* is a fastidious aquatic in its requirements, and unless it is satisfied it is liable to depart rapidly. It is especially important that the correct degree of acidity is maintained in the water, that the latter remains clear and does not become foul, and that it is as free as possible of algae, which inhibit the growth of this species.

It may be grown in a cool greenhouse, but growth here will tend to be slow, and the plant will become dormant in winter. It is better to keep it in a higher temperature, if possible maintaining a water temperature of between 70°F and 75°F (21–23·8°C), easily contrived with an electric aquarium heater. This will result in fast and continuous growth throughout the year. In the stovehouse such a heater would be unnecessary.

I prefer to use a rectangular rather than a round container. This should not be less than 12 by 10 by 6 inches (30 by 25·5 by 15 cm) deep. It could be a large plastic kitchen sink bowl or a fibreglass formal pool.

For every gallon (4·5 litres) of your container take a quarter teacup of moss peat together with (if possible) about six 4 inch (10 cm) lengths of the dead leaf of any species of *Typha*. Place the two ingredients in a saucepan of soft water, bring to the boil, and simmer for two minutes. When cool, pour into the container, and make up to the calculated capacity with pure soft water. As soon as the peat settles on the bottom and the water clears (2 or 3 days) the *Aldrovanda* is placed in the water.

The water should be a pale straw yellow, indicating that it is acid. This may be checked occasionally by placing a sample in a glass and viewing against a white background. If it is clear, or if it is green or cloudy remove as much water as possible, replacing with more soft water, or transfer the plants to a freshly prepared infusion as above. Too much sun or intense light encourages the formation of algae. A judiciously placed pot plant will provide shade from direct sun, though I like my plants to get a little early morning or evening sunlight. Should the build-up of a green scum of algal growth prove a problem this may easily be removed by laying sheets of paper flat on the surface of the water and then lifting them. Those wishing to create a natural pool effect will find the miniature Reedmace *Typha minima* a good associate which as a marginal will provide the necessary shade, and which seems beneficial to the plant. It will root easily in the peat substratum, and may be obtained fairly easily from aquatic nurseries.

Propagation Pieces of stem cut off the plant with three or more whorls of leaves will shoot and form new plants.

The Bladderworts

Aquatic species

General cultivation Well soaked granulated peat moss 1 inch (2·5 cm) deep is well firmed in an aquarium, glass bowl or other container. It may be secured with a thin layer of clean lime-free shingle, after which soft water is gently added with a fine rose so as not to disturb the peat. Immediately it is filled the plant may be floated on to the water. It should not be planted, for these are rootless, floating species. The position should be entirely sunless, and not even very light, or green filamentous algae (Blanket Weed, as it is also known) may grow, and a sunless window sill in the house is often the ideal place. After a fortnight, enough microscopic life will have accumulated to support the small 'water fleas' (*Daphnia*) which will provide the plants with prey and at the same time help to keep the water clear. These are best obtained in the form of 'Live *Daphnia*' from fish and aquarium shops, but may be obtained also—with an associated high risk of introducing filamentous algae—by introducing a jam jar of water taken from a clear pond. Species that form resting buds appreciate rather cool conditions in winter, though frost, on account of the breakable containers, must be avoided.

Should the dreaded algae develop, there is a simple method of killing it. Take 0·2 gram copper sulphate crystals (it is vital that this tiny quantity is accurately weighed on a chemical balance, and this may best be done by a pharmacist), and dissolve it in 18 fluid ounces (540 ml) of distilled water. Store this stock solution in bottles with non-metallic stoppers. Label the bottle 'POISON' together with the following directions: 'For control of algae in aquaria add one fluid ounce to each gallon of aquarium water. This quantity must not be exceeded', and lock it away from children. Failure to use the correct quantity may later cost you your plants.

Utricularia minor, U. gibba and *U. gibba exoleta* may be grown in small glass bowls or aquaria. The peat and water may be prepared exactly as directed for *Aldrovanda*, but excluding the *Typha* leaves. *U. minor* dies down to temporary resting buds in winter.

pp. 170, 171 *U. inflata* and *U. purpurea* are best in aquaria, though I have flowered
pp. 164, 169 the former in a large goldfish bowl. *U. vulgaris* should be grown in a large aquarium, or growth tends to be weak. This will also often grow well outside in ponds, but should be given the protection of other aquatic plants and floating lily leaves, without which it tends to fall prey to a small brown beetle. *U. intermedia* should be grown in 4 inches (10 cm) of water overlying 2 inches (5 cm) of peat (no shingle covering) in an aquarium. The peat should be raised to just above water level at the sides and sphagnum moss planted here. This should be allowed to grow into the water, while a little broken live sphagnum should be scattered into the water, thus creating conditions very similar to those in which the plant usually occurs in nature.

Epiphytic and similar South American species

The following species require positions shaded from strong sunlight. Either entirely shade from the sun from mid-morning to mid-afternoon, or cut light by over half with lath or other shading. Each is very suitable for a terrarium if placed 1 foot (30 cm) from fluorescent lights. All are easily propagated by division in early to mid-summer. If you find greenfly, these can be killed by submerging the plants entirely.

U. longifolia and *U. praelonga* are suitable for the cool greenhouse but grow even better in warm greenhouse temperatures. Either use 5 inch (13 cm) full length pots, or (in order to see the traps) upturned transparent polystyrene pots made from propagating domes, the light being blacked out from the compost with black polythene sheet (a black polythene folding pot is ideal). A few weeks later, traps will form against the polystyrene which may clearly be seen whenever the black cover is removed. Both species prefer to be very wet, and the pots may be immersed in summer to three quarters their depth in water. *U. praelonga* becomes dormant in winter, and the pots for both species should then be put to stand in shallow water. The compost should be pure live sphagnum moss, or long-fibre sphagnum with live sphagnum. pp. 172–3

U. reniformis will grow satisfactorily in a cool greenhouse if the winter temperature does not sink below 40°F (4·4°C), but does better in the warm greenhouse or in the stovehouse. The container should be a full length pot of at least a 5 inch (13 cm) size, but a wire basket is better on account of the wide-ranging root system. For compost, a mixture of orchid bark and live or long-fibre sphagnum moss is good, or pure live sphagnum may be used. Water by tray if potted, or by overhead watering if in a basket. p. 173

U. tricolor This amphibian species does well both in the cool and warm greenhouses. Put in a 4 or 5 inch (10 or 13 cm) dwarf pot in a compost of two parts live broken sphagnum moss, one part granulated moss peat and one part sand. Watering: once established it is best treated as a shallow aquatic, the water level being raised to up to $\frac{1}{4}$ inch (6 mm) above the surface of the compost.

U. endressii, U. alpina, U. dusenii and *U. calycifida* are all best in the warm greenhouse or stovehouse. Use a 5 inch (13 cm) full length pot and a compost of pure live broken sphagnum and orchid bark. Watering: tray. *U. calycifida* does well in rather dark, completely sunless places.

Amphibious species

U. racemosa (Japan) and *U. prehensilis* (S.E. Africa) will grow in a 5 inch (13 cm) dwarf pot with a compost of two parts broken sphagnum, live or long-fibre, one part moss peat and one part sand. Watering: after plants are established they are best treated as shallow aquatics; then raise water level to $\frac{1}{4}$ inch (6 mm) above the surface in the case of *U. racemosa*, and up to 2 inches (5 cm) in that of *U. prehensilis*. Cool greenhouse.

Species cultivation

Terrestrial species

The tiny grass-like leaves of some of these species are often hidden by moss growth. This is unimportant, and their continued existence is at once evident when they flower.

U. pubescens (U. peltata) Use a 4 inch (10 cm) dwarf pot and a compost of equal parts live or long-fibre broken sphagnum moss and granulated moss peat. Alternatively, two parts moss peat to one part sand. Watering: tray.

U. subulata will grow in a 4 or 5 inch (10 or 13 cm) dwarf pot and on compost of equal parts live broken sphagnum moss and granulated peat moss, with a little sand. Watering: tray.

p. 179 *U. lateriflora, U. novae-zealandiae, U. sandersonii* All are suitable for a 4 inch (10 cm) dwarf pot, with a compost of two parts moss peat to one part sand. Watering: tray. Cool greenhouse if temperature never drops below 40°F (4·4°C), or warm greenhouse. These plants often do well in windows in the house, if stood in saucers of water.

U. dichotoma, U. dichotoma uniflora and *U. violacea* Grow in a 4 inch (10 cm) dwarf pot, with a compost of two parts moss peat to one of sand. Watering: immerse until water is nearly at surface level. When established, raise it so that up to $\frac{1}{4}$ inch (6 mm) of water covers surface. Warm greenhouse.

p. 178 *U. menziesii* I have grown my plants for only two years. So far they have responded well to the following treatment, though they have not yet flowered. They are growing in a 4 inch (10 cm) dwarf pot, in a compost of equal parts broken sphagnum moss, moss peat and sand. Watering: immersion in water to within an inch (2·5 cm) of the surface. Cool greenhouse. The plant becomes dormant during the summer, springing into leaf again in late autumn or early winter. It is probably best to allow the pot of this corm-forming species to dry out during the dormant period, but I have not yet dared to try this.

The Pink Petticoats

p. 181 *Polypompholyx multifida* This annual comes easily from seed scattered over the surface of the compost in spring, and flowers profusely in the summer. Put in a 5 inch (13 cm) dwarf pot, in a compost of equal parts moss peat and sand. Watering: tray. Position: sunny with light shading, in a cool greenhouse. I have not grown *P. tenella*, but would expect it to respond to the same treatment.

Appendix 1

Raising *Sarracenia* hybrids

The extreme ease with which *Sarracenia* species and hybrids may be successfully cross-pollinated at random has its disadvantages, for it has led inevitably to the raising and retention of many inferior clones of often unknown or questionable parentage. These hardly further the future of the plant in horticulture and it is hoped that the following notes will assist those who want to try their hand at raising good plants of known identity—an always fascinating and rewarding hobby.

Flowering times

In order to effect a cross between two plants their flowering times must coincide, but this does not necessarily happen under normal conditions. Thus in *Sarracenia* the species may be roughly divided into three flowering groups consisting of early, midseason and late bloomers. The earliest consist of *S. flava, S. alata* and *S. oreophila*, the midseason of *S. purpurea* and *S. leucophylla*, while the lates are *S. rubra, S. psittacina* and *S. minor*. The flowering of one species with another in a group will often coincide, less often will that of early bloomers with midseasons, and rarely indeed will you find species in either of these groups in flower with the lates. Unless one is to depend on occasional 'freak' blooming, it is therefore necessary to artificially advance the flowering of the late bloomers or retard that of the earlier. This is not difficult, and becomes less so with experience. To advance, one places the plant in a warm place, removing it if and when the development of the stem appears to have caught up with that of the plant with which it is to be crossed. To retard, it is a matter of keeping the plant in a cool place. While it is ideal to have two greenhouses in which the temperatures may be varied, it is almost always possible to find suitable alternatives, such as a cold window of a room to retard, while a position near a heat source in the greenhouse, or the window of a warm room, may advance. Where it is possible to grow species out of doors during the winter this provides the ideal means of keeping them back, while late bloomers may be brought forward under glass.

Pollination procedure

This is basically simple. One to three days after opening pollen starts to be shed from the stamens of a bloom on to the floor of its umbrella-like pistil. Pick this up with a suitable instrument and transfer it to each of the five stigmas in another flower. For this I prefer to use the smallest size of water-colour brush with which I can carry sufficient pollen to give each stigma one light touch. To increase the likelihood of fertilization, the process should be repeated daily for as long as both blooms remain in flower. But to prevent the high risk of accidental fertilization with pollen from the wrong flower precautions must be taken. If the plants are growing out of doors the selected flowers should be protected from insect pollinators with a small muslin bag, and it is advisable where possible to bring them into a greenhouse. If they are growing under glass they will bloom too early for there to be a real risk of a visit from a suitable pollinating insect. A different brush must be used for each separate pollination. Thus, if you wish to cross *S. purpurea venosa* with *S. flava* to produce *S.* x *catesbaei*, it will increase your prospects of success to attempt to fertilize each bloom with the other, but you cannot do this with one brush, for in so doing you would risk fertilizing one or both blooms with their own pollen; consequently two brushes must be used, one for conveying pollen from *S. purpurea* to *S. flava*, the other from *S. flava* to *S. purpurea*. To prevent the possibility of confusion, always keep the brush in the pot of the pollen parent, poking the handle end into the compost so that the brush itself stands dry. After petal-fall, the brushes should be washed in cool soapy water, rinsed and dried before re-use.

Labelling

The moment a cross is made, it must be clearly recorded on a label, which is then inserted into the compost by the stem of the flower. At harvest time, any seed should be put in a clearly labelled and dated packet, and these details should also be entered yearly in a notebook. The name of the seed parent is entered first, followed by an 'x' and by the name of the pollinator. Thus if *S. flava* is pollinated by *S. purpurea venosa* it is written: *S. flava* x *S. purpurea venosa*, if *S. purpura venosa* by *S. flava* it is written: *S. purpurea venosa* x *S. flava*, though the resulting hybrid is the same in both cases. In practice, it saves time and space to use a code to denote the species; in fact without one it would be impossible to fit a record of the more complicated crosses on a label. The following are code letters for species as used by the author:

alata = *al*
rubra alabamensis = *ra*
oreophila = *or*
rubra jonesii = *rj*
minor = *m*
flava = *f*
rubra (typical) = *r*
psittacina = *ps*
purpurea venosa = *pv*
leucophylla = *d*
purpurea purpurea = *pp*

Thus *S. flava* x *S. purpurea venosa* becomes the simple formula *f* x *pv*.

Appendix 1

Each time a hybrid is crossed with another *Sarracenia* its identity is preserved in the formula with brackets. Thus if *f* x *pv* is pollinated with *d* it is written (*f* x *pv*) x *d*. When *f* x *pv* is pollinated by *m* x *ps* it is written (*f* x *pv*) x (*m* x *ps*), while if (*f* x *pv*) x *d* were pollinated by (*f* x *pv*) x (*m* x *ps*) it would be written [(*f* x *pv*) x *d*)] x [(*f* x *pv*) x (*m* x *ps*)]. These brackets are vitally important, for though without them the species that make up its ancestry are still evident, the proportion of their influence and their part in its pedigree are not. Thus *ps* x *d* x *m* x *f* x *pv could* be *ps* x (*d* x *m*) x (*f* x *pv*) in which the influence of *ps* as one parent would be great, or it might be [*ps* x*d*) x *m*] x (*f* x *pv*), in which its influence would be little, or any of a large number of other combinations. It is obvious that the ancestry of a hybrid may be so complex that the formula itself will be too long to fit on a label. It will then be better to label the plant with a number and to enter this number in the record book together with the formula.

Subspecies and distinct forms will have considerable influence on the appearance of a hybrid. Thus, *f* x *pp* will have narrower pitchers which will be often more vividly coloured than *f* x *pv*. It is therefore important to distinguish them. To do this I attach a small additional letter to indicate a subspecies and a capital letter for a form or variety. Thus *ra* is *S. rubra alabamensis*, while *rG* indicates *S. rubra* Gulf Coast Form. The full meanings of these letters should of course be entered in your record book.

Programme

Instead of pollinating flowers at random whenever the opportunity arises, it is best to have a distinct plan. To start with it would be sensible to concentrate on raising the simple interspecies hybrids. Your second step could be more enterprising. You may, for example, have raised some *S.* x *mitchelliana* (*d* x *pv*) and may admire its pitcher variegation but prefer more of the grace and coloration of *S. leucophylla*. In this case you will cross the latter with the hybrid. It is then advisable to prick out as many as possible of the seedlings, and to grow these on until they are at least semi-mature before selecting those which appear to be most outstanding. With luck, you may find amongst these the very plant you desired. On the other hand, if all the seedlings are too near to *S. leucophylla* in habit, you may get your ideal by crossing these back with *S.* x *mitchelliana*. All this takes time, but it is satisfying enough to watch one's hybrid seedlings grow, and if one or more crosses are attempted annually, the time comes when there is always something new reaching maturity.

Appendix 2

Triphyophyllum – a passive flypaper

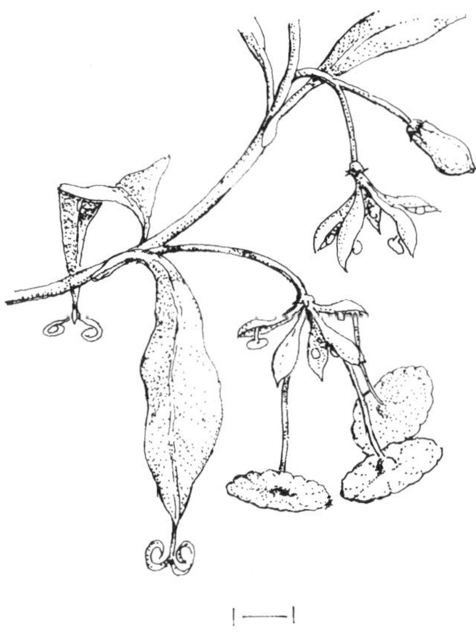

Fruit of *Triphyophyllum peltatum*, showing three stages in development and the winged seed.

Triphyophyllum (try-fyo-fillum) Fam. Dioncophyllaceae
Since writing the original text for this volume, evidence has been published which strongly suggests that another genus of plant may be carnivorous, in this case during a single stage of its life.* Absolute proof of carnivory—that the products of digestion are absorbed into the plant's system for its benefit—would be required to include the genus in the main body of this book, but the degree of probability merits its inclusion as an appendix. *Triphyophyllum peltatum*, the only known species, is a tropical woody climber native to the rain forests of Sierra Leone, Liberia and the Ivory Coast. Highly selective in habitat, it occurs within very limited areas. This may well be its undoing, for these very forestlands are now subject to wholesale destruction by man, and already the species appears to be on the threshold of extinction.

The plant is remarkable in producing three distinctly different types of leaf. The non-climbing juvenile shoot is up to a yard (metre) high, and on this two kinds of leaf occur spirally with short internodes. The first to be produced is slender and lance-shaped, up to about 14 inches (35·5 cm) long by 2 inches (5·1 cm) wide, non-glandular and of ordinary appearance. The second type of leaf is very different, for its more or less upright leaves are partly or entirely thread-like and glandular. It is this kind which is believed to be carnivorous, and which we will consider in more detail. The third type occurs on the mature climbing stem which, after two or more years, commences to grow from a bud at the end of the juvenile shoot. These are the smallest leaves, being up to 7 inches long (17·8 cm) by 1½ inches (3·75 cm) wide, and they are separated by long internodes. Each is lance-shaped, with a strong midrib which divides at the end of the leaf into two hooks by which means the plant finds support on other vegetation on its long climb to the treetops. Here, sprays of small fragrant white flowers are borne from leaf axils, followed by fruiting bodies from which hang the curiously winged seeds. The seed is seated centrally in the wing, and the latter is flat and saucer-shaped with an upturned edge, the whole being about 4 inches (10 cm) in diameter. This dispersal device is an attractive object, vividly coloured pink to red, and on release it glides, often conveying the seed for a considerable distance.

The glandular leaf may be entirely thread-like, or may often be

*Sally Green, et al, 'Seasonal heterophylly and leaf gland features in *Triphyophyllum*' in *Botanical Journal of the Linnean Society*, 78, (1979)
Airy Shaw, H. K., 'On the Dioncophyllaceae, a remarkable new family of flowering plants' in *Kew Bulletin* 6, No. 3, (1951)

transitional, a portion of the upper part being thread-like and a variable part of the lower being flat and non-glandular. The thread-like blade is rolled when young in the manner of *Drosera filiformis*, unwinding in a similar fashion, and it is equipped with both stalked and sessile glands. The former are reddish, in two intermixed sizes, the larger being $\frac{1}{8}$ inch (2–3 mm), the smaller being up to about $\frac{1}{20}$ inch (1 mm) high. Both bear droplets of a viscid secretion on which flying and sometimes crawling victims are trapped. The presence of the insect stimulates the secretion of more fluid not only from these but also from the hitherto dry sessile glands. The victim struggles and in so doing may touch neighbouring sticky glands. In turn the sessile glands beneath these are activated, and it is not long before the creature is stifled by the accumulation of viscid fluid. Already some digestive enzymes have been identified in this liquid (proteases, peroxidase and esterase), a fact which, together with the surprising structural similarity of the glands to those found in the unrelated family Droseraceae, can leave little doubt that we have here a newly discovered carnivorous genus. If so, the question naturally arises as to why it should adopt this habit during one stage only of its life. The soil in which it grows is poor, and deficient in potash, and it may be significant that it does so before commencing to form its often immensely long adult stem which ultimately produces the flowers, and this may provide the means of correcting any mineral deficiencies in its system before entering this final stage of its growth.

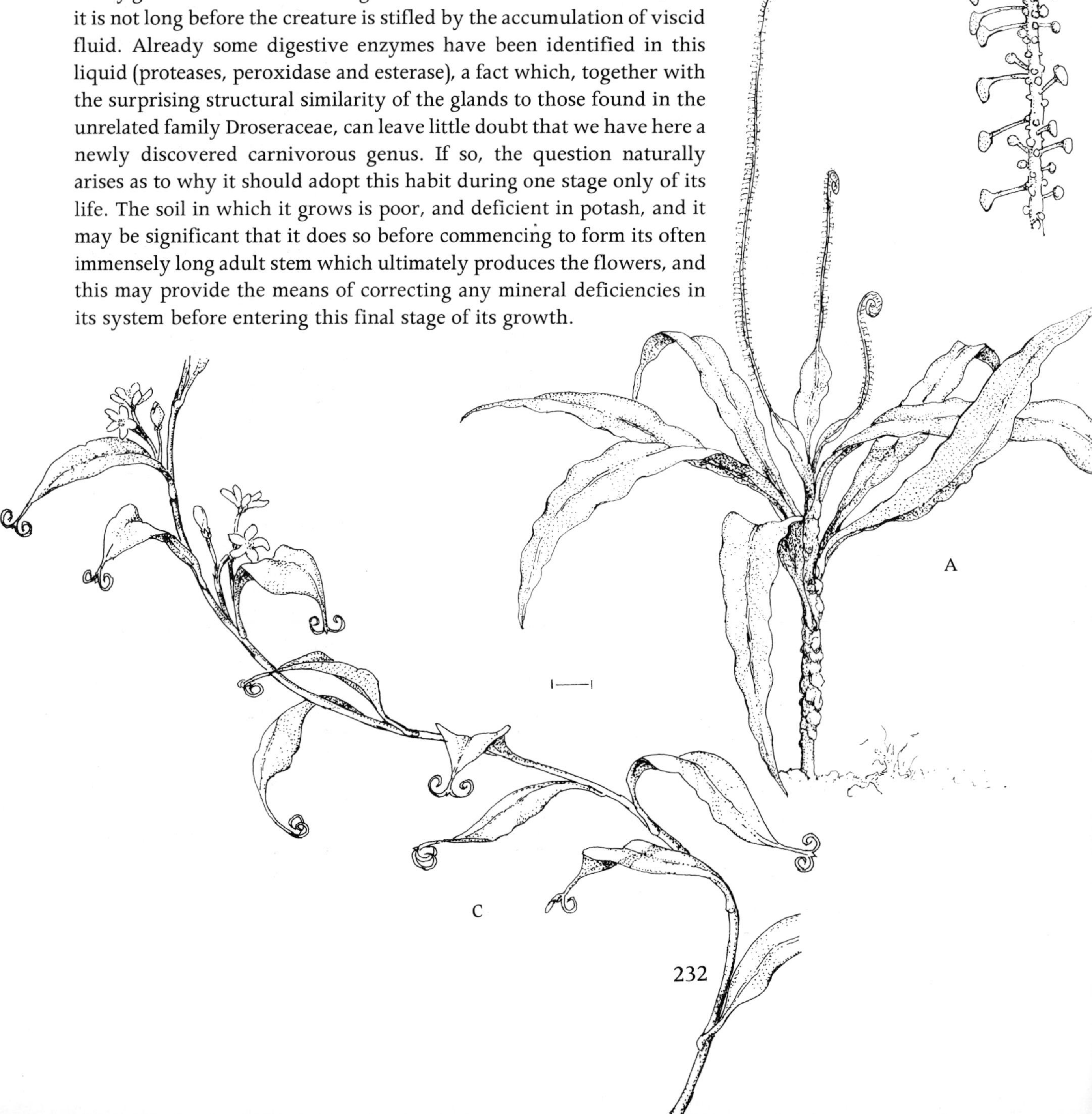

Triphyophyllum. A: juvenile shoot with lance-shaped and glandular leaves. B: detail of part of glandular leaf. C: mature climbing shoot showing hooked leaves and flowers.

Appendix 3 Nepenthes Horticultural Hybrids

To cover this subject adequately would demand the publication of a major specialized work, and these plants are beyond the scope of this volume. However, many magnificent plants are to be found in their ranks and a rebirth of interest is now evident in both Europe and America. Knowledge of the parentage and raisers of the named hybrids is, however, frequently confused, sketchy, or difficult to come by. The lists published in *The Carnivorous Plant Newsletter* Vol 8, March 1979 will do much to rectify this situation, and I am grateful to the editors of that journal for permission to reproduce them. I must acknowledge the excellent research of R. Fleming in preparing the abbreviated list below.

NAME	PARENTAGE
Amabilis	*(rafflesiana* x *ampullaria)* x *rafflesiana*
Allardii	*veitchii* x *maxima*
Amesiana	*rafflesiana* x *(rafflesiana* x *ampullaria)*
Dr. Edgar Anderson	*[(rafflesiana* x *gracilis)* x *(rafflesiana* x *ampullaria)]* x *[rafflesiana* x *gracilis]*
Atropurpurea	*sanguinea* x *maxima 'superba'*
Alliottii	*northiana* x *maxima*
Atro-sanguinea	*(distillatoria* x *gracilis)* x *khasiana*
Balfouriana	*(northiana* x *maxima)* x *(sanguinea* x *khasiana)*
Bohnickii	*[(northiana* x *maxima)* x *maxima]* x *[(northiana* x *maxima)* x *maxima]*
Boissiana	*[maxima* x *veitchii]* x *[mirabilis* x *(rafflesiana* x *ampullaria)]*
Boissiense	*gracilis* x *[(gracilis* x *khasiana)* x *(rafflesiana* x *ampullaria)]*
Caroli-schmidtii	*(northiana* x *maxima)* x *(veitchii* x *maxima)*
Chelsonii	*(rafflesiana* x *gracilis)* x *(rafflesiana* x *ampullaria)*
Chelsonii excellens	*rafflesiana* x *[(rafflesiana* x *gracilis)* x *(rafflesiana* x *ampullaria)]*
Coccinea	*(rafflesiana* x *ampullaria)* x *mirablis*
Compacta	*(rafflesiana* x *ampullaria)* x *mirabilis*
Courtii	*gracilis* x *(rafflesiana* x *gracilis)*
Joseph Cutak	*[(rafflesiana* x *gracilis)* x *(rafflesiana* x *ampullaria)]* x *[rafflesiana* x *gracilis]*
Cylindrica	*distillatoria 'rubra'* x *veitchii*
Deslogesii	*(maxima* x *veitchii)* x *(northiana* x *maxima)*
Dicksoniana	*rafflesiana* x *veitchii*
Dominii	*rafflesiana* x *gracilis*
Dormanniana	*mirabilis* x *(gracilis* x *khasiana)*
Dyeriana	*(northiana* x *maxima)* x *(rafflesiana* x *veitchii)*
Edinensis	*rafflesiana* x *[(rafflesiana* x *gracilis)* x *(rafflesiana* x *ampullaria)]*
Excelsa	*veitchii* x *sanguinea*
Excelsior	*rafflesiana* x *(rafflesiana* x *ampullaria)*
Eyermanni	*mirabilis* x *(rafflesiana* x *ampullaria)*
Dr. D C Fairburn	*[(rafflesiana* x *gracilis)* x *(rafflesiana* x *ampullaria)]* x *[rafflesiana* x *gracilis]*
Formosa	*[(rafflesiana* x *gracilis)* x *(rafflesiana* x *ampullaria)]* x *distillatoria*
Fournieri	*northiana* x *maxima*
Gamerii	*(maxima 'superba'* x *veitchii)* x *(northiana* x *maxima)*
Gautieri	*northiana* x *maxima*
Goebelii	*(northiana* x *maxima)* x *maxima*
Goettingensis	*(northiana* x *maxima)* x *(rafflesiana* x *veitchii)*
Grandis	*maxima 'superba'* x *northiana 'pulchra'*
Harryana	*edwardsiana* x *villosa*
Henryana	*(gracilis* x *khasiana)* x *(rafflesiana* x *ampullaria)*
Hibberdii	*(rafflesiana* x *ampullaria)* x *(gracilis* x *khasiana)*
Hoeischeri	*(northiana* x *maxima)* x *([gracilis* x *(rafflesiana* x *gracilis)]* x *distillatoria 'rubra')*
Hookerae	*rafflesiana* x *mirabilis*
Hookeriana	*rafflesiana* x *ampullaria*
Nel Horner	*[(rafflesiana* x *gracilis)* x *(rafflesiana* x *ampullaria)]* x *[rafflesiana* x *gracilis]*
Hybrida	*khasiana* x *gracilis*
Hybrida maculata	*khasiana* x *gracilis*
Hybrida maculata elongata	*gracilis* x *(rafflesiana* x *gracilis)*
Intermedia	*gracilis* x *rafflesiana*
Kinabaluensis	*rajah* x *villosa*
Krausii	*(northiana* x *maxima)* x *(veitchii* x *maxima)*
Ladenburgii	*(northiana* x *maxima)* x *maxima*
Lawrenciana	*mirablilis* x *(rafflesiana* x *ampullaria)*
Longicaudata	*maxima 'superba'* x *northiana 'pulchra'*
Lyrata	*(khasiana* x *gracilis)* x *rafflesiana*
Dr. John MacFarlane	*sanguinea* x *maxima 'superba'*
Maria-Louisa	*northiana* x *maxima*
Mastersiana	*sanguinea* x *khasiana*
Mercieri	*northiana* x *maxima*
Merrilliata	*merrilliana* x *alata*
Mixta	*northiana* x *maxima*
F. W. Moore	*(northiana* x *maxima)* x *(rafflesiana* x *veitchii)*
Director G. T. Moore	*[(rafflesiana* x *gracilis)* x *(rafflesiana* x *ampullaria)]* x *[rafflesiana* x *gracilis]*
Katharine Moore	*(rafflesiana* x *gracilis)* x *(rafflesiana* x *ampullaria)* x *[rafflesiana* x *gracilis]*
Morganiana	*mirabilis* x *(rafflesiana* x *ampullaria)*
Neufvilliana	*(northiana* x *maxima)* x *maxima*
Nobilis	*sanguinea* x *maxima 'superba'*
Outramiana	*(gracilis* x *khasiana)* x *(rafflesiana* x *ampullaria)*
Paradisae	*mirabilis* x *(rafflesiana* x *ampullaria)*
Patersonii	*mirabilis* x *(rafflesiana* x *ampullaria)*
Paullii	*(maxima 'superba'* x *veitchii)* x *(northiana* x *maxima)*
Petersii	*(northiana* x *maxima)* x *(veitchii* x *maxima)*
Picturata	*(northiana* x *maxima)* x *(rafflesiana* x *veitchii)*
Pitcheri	*[mirabilis* x *(rafflesiana* x *ampullaria)]* x *[(gracilis* x *khasiana)* x *(rafflesiana* x *ampullaria)]*
Lieutenant R B Pring	*[(rafflesiana* x *gracilis)* x *(rafflesiana* x *ampullaria)]* x *[rafflesiana* x *gracilis]*
Rafflesiana pallida	*(khasiana* x *gracilis)* x *rafflesiana*
Ratcliffiana	*mirabilis* x *(rafflesiana* x *ampullaria)*
Remilliensis	*(northiana* x *maxima)* x *(veitchii* x *maxima)*
Reutheri	*(northiana* x *maxima)* x *(sanguinea* x *khasiana)*
Robusta	*mirabilis* x *(rafflesiana* x *ampullaria)*
Roedigeri	*(northiana* x *maxima)* x *maxima*
Rubro-maculata	*(khasiana* x *gracilis)* x *veitchii*
Rufescens	*[gracilis* x *(rafflesiana* x *gracilis)]* x *distillatoria 'rubra'*
Rutzii	*(northiana* x *maxima)* x *(veitchii* x *maxima)*
Saint Louis	*[(rafflesiana* x *gracilis)* x *(rafflesiana* x *ampullaria)]* x *[rafflesiana* x *gracilis]*
Sedenii	*gracilis* x *khasiana*
Henry Shaw	*[(rafflesiana* x *gracilis)* x *(rafflesiana* x *ampullaria)]* x *[rafflesiana* x *gracilis]*
Siebrechitiana	*mirabilis* x *(gracilis* x *khasiana)*
Siebertii	*(northiana* x *maxima)* x *(veitchii* x *maxima)*
Simonii	*northiana* x *maxima*
Shinjuku	*[northiana* x *maxima]* x *[mirabilis* x *(rafflesiana* x *ampullaria)]*
Sprendida	*mirabilis* x *(rafflesiana* x *ampullaria)*
Stammieri	*[(northiana* x *maxima)* x *maxima]* x *[(northiana* x *maxima)* x *maxima]*
Stewartii	*mirabilis* x *(rafflesiana* x *ampullaria)*
Superba	*(gracilis* x *khasiana)* x *(rafflesiana* x *ampullaria)*
Tiveyi	*maxima 'superba'* x *veitchii*
Gerald Ulrichi	*(rafflesiana* x *gracilis)* x *(rafflesiana* x *ampullaria)*
Vallierae	*(maxima 'superba'* x *veitchii)* x *(northiana* x *maxima)*
Ventrata	*ventricosa* x *alata*
Williamsii	*(gracilis* x *khasiana)* x *(rafflesiana* x *ampullaria)*
Wittei	*maxima* x *stenophylla*
Wrigleyana	*mirabilis* x *(rafflesiana* x *ampullaria)*
?	*thorelii* x *(maxima* x *stenophylla)*

Bibliography and References

1 Barber, J. T. & C. P., 'Mucilaginous seed pellicles' in *What's New in Plant Physiology* No 6 (1976)

Barber, J. T., 'Mucilaginous seeds—interactions with micro-organisms'. Abstract in *Plant Physiology* 59 No. 6 (June 1977)

2 McMillan, P., 'Some thoughts and observations on Sarracenia' in *Carnivorous Plant Newsletter* Vol 7, No. 4, p. 105 (1978)

3 Folkerts, R., 'Mississippi Field Trip' in *Carnivorous Plant Newsletter* Vol 4, No. 2, p. 33 (1975)

4 Case, F. W. & R. B., *Rhodora* (New England Botanical Club, Inc. Mass) 76, No. 808, pp. 650–5 (1974), & 78, No. 814, pp. 270–325

5 Schnell, D. E., 'Interspecific variation in *Sarracenia rubra*' in *Castanea* (Journal of Southern Appalachian Botanical Club) 42, pp. 149–70 (1977)

6 Curtis' *Botanical Magazine* Tab 780 (1804)

7 Schnell, D. E., *Carnivorous Plants of the United States and Canada*. Blaire (1976)

8 Walcott, M. V., *The North American Pitcher Plants*. Smithsonian Institute (1933). See 'Distribution of North American Pitcher Plants' by Dr E. T. Wherry

9 Lloyd, F. E., *The Carnivorous Plants*, Chronica Botanica Co. (1942) and Dover Publications Inc., New York (1976)

10 *Gardeners Chronicle* Vol. XIII, New Series, Feb 14, 1880, p. 200 and Feb 28, 1880, p. 264

11 Darwin, Erasmus, *The Botanic Garden*. London (1791)

12 Bartram, W., *Travels in North and South Carolina, Georgia and Florida*. Philadelphia (1791)

13 Hooker, H. D., 'Mechanics of movement in *Drosera rotundifolia*' in *Bulletin Torrey Botanical Club*, New York, 43, p. 1 (1916), 44, p. 389 (1917)

14 Ecklon and Zeyher, '*D. cistiflora* var. *multiflora*' in Curtis' *Botanical Magazine* Tab 7100 (1890)

15 Everhard, B. and Morley, B. D., *Wild Flowers of the World*, Ebury Press and Michael Joseph London (1970)

16 Erickson, E., *Plants of Prey*. Lamb Publications, Osborne Park, Western Australia (1968)

17 Rose, S., *Carnivorous Plant Newsletter* Vol 7, No. 2 p. 28 (1977)

See also:

Bentham, G., '*Heliamphora nutans*' in *Transactions of the Linnean Society* 18, pp. 429–33 (1840)

Green, S., Green, T. L. and Heslop-Harrison, Y., 'Seasonal heterophylly and leaf gland features in *Triphyophyllum* (Dioncophyllaceae), a new carnivorous plant genus' in *Botanical Journal of the Linnean Society* 78, pp. 99–116 (1979)

Heslop-Harrison, Y., 'Carnivorous Plants' in *Scientific American* 238, 2: pp. 104–16 (1978)

Hooker, J. D., 'On the origin and development of the pitcher of *Nepenthes*' in *Linnean Society Transactions* 22, pp. 415–24 (1859)

Hooker, W. J., '*Ultricularia nelumbifolia*' in *Icones Plantarum* 6, DV–DVI (1843)

Jones, F. M., 'Pitcherplants and their insect associates' in Walcott, M. V., *Illustrations of North American Pitcher Plants*, Smithsonian Institute (1935)

Macfarlane, J. M., 'Nepenthaceae' in Engler, A., *Das Pflanzenreich* IV, iii, pp. 1–92 (1908)

Maguire, B., 'Sarraceniaceae' in *Memoirs of the NY Botanic Gardens* 29, pp. 36–62 (1978)

Mody, N. V., Henson, R., Hedin, P. A., Kokpol, U. and Miles, D. H., 'Isolation of the insect paralysing agent Coniine from *Sarracenia flava*' in *Specialia* 32, 7, ii, pp. 829–30 (1976)

Slack, A., *Insect-eating Plants and how to grow them*. London, Washington (1986)

Stephens, E. L., 'A new Sundew, *Drosera regia* (Stephens) from Cape Province' in *Transactions of the Royal Society of South Africa* 13, pp. 309–12 (1926)

Steyermark, J. A., 'Sarraceniaceae' in *Fieldiana* 28, i, pp. 239–42

Sydenham, P. H. and Findlay, G. P., 'Rapid movement of the bladder of *Utricularia*' in *Australian Journal of Biological Science* 26, pp. 1115–26 (1973)

Williams, S. E., 'Comparative Sensory Physiology of the Droseraceae – The Evolution of a Plant Sensory System' in *Proceedings of the American Philosophical Society*, Vol 120, No. 2, pp. 187–203 (June 1976)

Wood, C. E. Jr., 'The genera of Sarraceniaceae and Droseraceae in the Southeast USA' in *Journal of the Arnold Arboretum* 41, pp. 152–63

List of Suppliers

Nurseries

World Insectivorous Plants, P.O. Box 303, Grant, Florida 32949, USA
Marcel Lecoufle, 5, rue de Paris, 94470, Boissy-St-Leger, France
Harald Weiner, Kaiserstr. 74, 3250 Hameln 1, West Germany

Sphagnum Moss Live

Peter Pauls Nurseries, Canandaigua, N.Y. 14424, USA
Joseph Bentley Ltd, Barrow-on-Humber, South Humberside, DN19 7AQ, England

Sphagnum Moss, Long-Fibre and Milled

World Insectivorous Plants, P.O. Box 303, Grant, Florida 32949, USA

Pine Bark

Burnham Nurseries Ltd, Kingsteignton, Newton Abbot, Devon, England
Rod McLellan Co., 1450, El Camino Real, South San Francisco, CA 94080, USA
Bas van Buuren B.V., Koningen Julianaweg No 2, Maasland, Holland
Evelyn Rölke, Von Möller Strasse 25c, D-4800 Bielefeld 14, W. Germany

Perlite

Carnivorous Gardens, P.O. Box 331, Hamilton, N.Y. 13346, USA
Marston Exotics, Spring Gardens, Frome, Somerset BA11 2NZ, England

Misting Systems

Humex Ltd, 5, High Road, Byfleet, Surrey, England
Lord & Burnham, Irvington-on-Hudson, New York, N.Y. 10533, USA

Blinds

See Humex and Lord & Burnham (above)

Propagators, Heated

See Humex, also Rod McLellan (above)

Propagators, Unheated

Many kinds available at garden centres in Britain
Propagator covers to fit pots made by Stewart Plastics Ltd, Purley Way, Croydon, Surrey, England

Plant Troughs

Stewart Plastics Ltd (above), also Rod McLellan (above)

Table Conservatories, Terrariums

Peter Pauls Nurseries (above)

Lighted Plant Trays

Emblem Sunshine Garden: enquire from Sale Tilney International Ltd, Weybridge Trading Estate, Weybridge, Surrey, England
Peter Pauls Nurseries (above)

Carnivorous Plant Societies and Journals

The International Carnivorous Plant Society, c/o The Fullerton Arboretum, Dept of Biology, California State University, Fullerton, CA 92634, USA. The society has a quarterly journal and seed exchange scheme.
The Carnivorous Plant Society, c/o Malcolm Goddard, 24 Osborne Road, Brentwood, Essex, England. The society publishes a Journal and runs a seed exchange scheme.
The Carnivorous Plant Society in Germany, c/o Metin A. Savignano, Mühlrain 26, 7000 Stuttgart 1, West Germany

Glossary

Anther end part of stamen which bears the pollen.

Anthocyanins complex substances responsible for the colours of numerous plants and flowers (e.g. red venation in *Sarracenia*).

Apex end of a part of a plant which is furthest from its point of attachment.

Areola (pl. *areolae*) small pit; also used for the translucent 'windows' in upper pitchers of *Darlingtonia* and of some *Sarracenias*.

Axil angle between stem and upper surface of leaf stalk growing from the stem.

Bracts small modified leaves often found at base of, or along flowering stems, and sometimes near or on the calyx as in *Sarracenia*.

Calyx the outer group of parts of the flower, consisting of the sepals.

Chitin the hard material of which the skeleton and wings of insects are composed.

Chlorophyll the green colouring matter of plants which enables them to manufacture carbohydrates from carbon-dioxide and water by using energy derived from sunlight.

Circinate rolled inwards from apex to base like a watch-spring, as in the embryo leaves of many ferns.

Clone all plants obtained by vegetative propagation from one seedling are said to be of the same clone.

Column the neck-like portion of the lowest part of the hood in many *Sarracenias*.

Corolla the collective name for the petals of one flower.

Corymb an inflorescence in which the branches and flower stalks are of different lengths which become increasingly shorter up the stem, so that the flowers are all held on the same level (e.g. Elder).

Cuticle a waxy, waterproof material forming the external layer of the epidermal cells.

Decumbent lying on the ground, but with the apex or tip turning upwards.

Dichotomous repeatedly dividing into two branches.

Diffusion the passage of molecules of a substance in solution from a liquid where they are in high concentration to one where they are in low concentration.

Dropper shoot which in some seedling *Droseras* is sent down into the soil from near the base of the stem, the growing tip then forming a tuber at a suitable depth.

Enzymes substances produced by and found in living cells. They are also found in digestive juices of animals and carnivorous plants, each having power to break down specific substances.

Epiphyte (adj. epiphytic) a plant which grows on another plant but is not a parasite.

Epidermis living cells which form the thin surface layer, usually one cell thick, on leaves and young shoots.

Fauna a collective term for animals inhabiting one place.

Form a plant displaying an inherited characteristic differing from the typical species or variety. However, it is not sufficiently stable or marked to justify the rank of variety.

Gemma (pl. *gemmae*) a small body produced by the parent plant by non-sexual means which, when detached, may form a new individual.

Genus (pl. *genera*) a category of closely related species; the generic name is given as the first of the two names of each species.

Gland a structure of one or many cells which secretes a substance.

Hibernaculum (pl. *hibernacula*) a winter resting bud formed when the main plant dies back, and from which the plant regenerates in suitable conditions. It is often rootless.

Hood lid-like appendage hanging over or above the opening of many pitcher-leaves.

Hypha, hyphal thread (pl. *hyphae*) one filament of the vegetable body of a fungus.

Inferior said of the ovary when the sepals, petals and stamens appear to spring from the top of it.

Inflorescence flowering branch or flowering part of the plant above the stem-leaves. Includes branches, bracts and flowers.

Interspecies that which is between two species (e.g. an interspecies cross resulting in a hybrid).

Linear leaf one which is narrow with near-parallel sides.

Midrib the main vein of a leaf running centrally and longitudinally through the blade.

Morphology the form and structure of an organism.

Mucilage glue-like organic compounds of vegetable origin and complex structure.

Mucilaginous containing or pertaining to mucilage.

Mutant an organism in which the characteristics have been changed by alteration of its hereditary material.

Mycelium the mass of fine threads or *hyphae* which forms the vegetable body of fungus and which seeks and absorbs nutriment.

Mycorrhiza a mutually beneficial association between the root cells of a plant and the mycelium of a fungus. Often called a mycorrhizal association.

Ovary container in which seeds are formed.

Panicle a branched raceme.

Parasite an organism which lives in or on another, obtaining nourishment from it without being of service to its host.

Pedicel a stalk which is the last branch of an inflorescence, bearing the flower or fruit.

Peltate a leaf or other flattened structure in which the stalk is attached to the undersurface.

Persitome in *Nepenthes*, a plate inserted on the rim of the mouth in most species. It is down-curved on both sides, and thus semi-cylindrical in section, and ribbed, the ribs being usually sharply toothed on the inner margin.

Petiole the leaf-stalk.

pH a logarithmic index for the concentration of hydrogen ions in a solution. A reading below pH 7·0 indicates acidity, one above pH 7·0 indicates alkalinity.

Photosynthesis the synthesis by plants of carbohydrates and more complex substances from carbon dioxide and water using the energy from light through the agency of chlorophyll.

Phyllode (pl. *phyllodia*) leaf-like structures. In *Sarracenia* these are predominantly widened petioles.

Pistil the female part of a flower comprising the ovary, style and stigma.

Protozoa (sing. *protozoan*) single-celled microscopic animals found in great numbers in both salt and fresh water, and in deep soil.

Raceme an inflorescence consisting of a single main stem along which the flowers are borne on pedicels.

Reflexed turned backwards abruptly.

Revolute that which is rolled inwards.

Rhizoid root-like structure with the appearance and function of a root.

Rhizome an underground root-like stem bearing scale-leaves and at least one bud.

Saprophyte an organism which obtains its food from dead organic materials.

Scale, scale leaf a leaf greatly reduced in size and scale-like, usually sessile and seldom green.

Scape a leafless flowering stem extending from a rosette of leaves or root itself to the flower or inflorescence.

Secretory secretion-forming.

Sepal one of the leaf-like or petal-like members which make up the calyx of the flower.

Sessile attached without a stalk.

Species a group of mutually fertile and closely allied plants displaying differences from other related plants.

Stamen part of the flower which produces pollen, usually consisting of a filament which bears the anther.

Stigma the end of the style to which pollen must be transferred in order to germinate and bring about fertilization.

Stipule one of the two leaf-like appendages which are often present at the base of petiole.

Stolon in *Utricularia* this refers to the underground stems of terrestrial and epiphytic species.

Style the part of the pistil between the ovary and stigma.

Superior said of the ovary when it is placed above the level of the sepals, petals and stamens in the structure of the flower (opp. inferior).

Symbiosis an internal link between two organisms which is to their mutual advantage.

Tuber a swollen underground stem, or occasionally a root, used to store food material.

Turion the hibernaculum or winter resting bud containing food, formed by many water plants including some of the aquatic *Utricularias*.

Variety a large number of individuals which differ from others in that species and breed true from seed.

Velum in *Utricularia* a thin membrane which helps to seal the door by filling the chink below the lower edge of door and threshold.

Venation the veins of an organ as a whole or their arrangement.

Vernation the manner in which the leaf is packed in the bud.

Whorl a group in which identical organs (e.g. leaves) are arranged around the stem in a circle.

Index

Numbers in italic refer to illustrations

Acids 13, 30, 78, 167
adaptations 11
Alabama Canebrake Pitcher Plant 46
Aldrovanda vesiculosa 15, 17, 19, 161–3, 190, 223–4
Alpine Butterwort 113
Amadei, C. 161
amylase 30, 110
antennae, *Utricularia* 166, 172
anthocyanin 47, 50
ants 30, 42, 58, 78, 91
areolae 56, *57*, 59, *61*, *70*, 72, 90, 91
Ashida, J. 163

Bacterial decay 13, 20, 23, 30–1, 48, 73, 78, 160
Bailey, F. M. 79
Barber, J. T. & C. P. 18
Bartram, W. 26, 37, 119, 156
Batalin, A. 122
bladderworts 15, 18, 19, 165ff., 224–7
Botrytis cinerea 199–200, 212, 213–4, 219, 223
Bridal Rainbow Sundew 143, 146
Brackenridge, J. D. 71
buds, winter resting 104, 111–13, 125ff., 168
Burbidge, F. W. 82
butterwort 15, 16–17, 19, 103, 104ff.
Byblidaceae 95
Byblis 15, 16, 19, 95–8
  gigantea 95, 96–8, 207
  liniflora 95, 98, 207

Canby, W. M. 28
Cape Sundew 136, 214, 215, 218
Capsella bursa-pastoris seeds 18
Carnivorous Plant Society, The 9, 235
Case, F. W. & R. B. 44
Catesby, M. 31
Cephalotaceae 89
Cephalotus follicularis 15, 19, *88*, 89ff., 206
chitinase 79
Cistus Flowered Sundew 136, 218
Clemesha, S. 89. 152
Clusius 26, 46, 49
Cobra Lily 15, 19, 21, 28, *70*, 71ff., 188, *189*, 201–2
coldhouse 188
Collinson, P. 155
Collinson, T. 49
Common Butterwort 104, 110, 111–12, 193, 211
Common Scarlet Sundew 141, 219
compost 185, 195
coniine 30
containers 193–4
Contasano, J. 202, 203
coolhouse 187
crocking 195
cultivation, *Aldrovanda* 223–4
  Byblis 207–8
  Cephalotus 206
  Darlingtonia 201–2
  Dionaea 222–3
  Drosera 213–21
  Drosophyllum 208–9
  greenhouse 186
  Heliamphora 196–7
  indoor 183–6
  Nepenthes 202–6
  outdoor 190–3
  Pinguicula 210–13
  Polypompholyx 227
  Sarracenia 197–200
  Utricularia 224–7

Dactylella 18
Danser, B. H. 80
Darlington, W. 71
Darlingtonia californica 15, 19, 21, 28, *70*, 71ff., 188, *189*, 201–2
Darwin, Charles 11, 28, 104, 119, 152, 156, 160, 172
Darwin, Erasmus 119
de l'Obel 56
d'Entrecasteau 89
'Dewy Pine' 100
digestion, in *Aldrovanda* 163
  in *Cephalotus* 91
  in *Darlingtonia* 73
  in *Dionaea* 160
  in *Drosera* 121, 122
  in *Drosophyllum* 100
  in *Heliamphora* 23
  in *Nepenthes* 78–9
  in *Pinguicula* 107, 110
  in *Sarracenia* 30–1
  in *Utricularia* 167–8
Dionaea muscipula 15, 17–18, 19, *154*, 155–60, 184, 193, 222–3
Dobbs, Arthur 155
'dropper' 141
Drosera 15, 17, 19, 103, 119ff., 185, 190, 213–21
  adelae 147, 184, 186, 214, 221
  aliciae *10*, *124*, 134, *135*, 184, 215, 218
  androsacea 219
  anglica 128, *129*, 193, 214, 216, *217*
  auriculata 144, 220
  'Bannister' 140, 218, 219
  'Beermullah' 219
  binata C. V. 150, 184, 215
  binata var. *dichotoma* 148, 150, 151–2, 184, 215, 221
    'Giant Type' *123*, *151*, 152, 184, *191*, 215, 221
    'Small Type' 151–2, 184, 215, 221
  binata var. *multifida* 152–3, 184, 215, 221
    'Extrema' 152–3, 184, 215, 222
    'Pink Form' 153, 184, 215, 222
  binata 'T Form' 148–50, 184, 193, 215, 221
  brevifolia 216
  burmanii 121, 134, 218
  x *californica* 216
  capensis 136, *137*, 214, 215, 218
  capillaris 133, 218
  cistiflora 136, 218
  cuneifolia 134, 184, 218
  dichrosepala *138*, 139, *158*, 219
  x *dinata* 222
  drummondii 140
  erythrorhiza 143
  filiformis 130, 214
    ssp. *filiformis* *125*, 130, 193, 216
    ssp. *tracyi* 130, 188, 216
  gigantea 146, 220
  glanduligera 141, 219
  hamiltonii *142*, 143, 215
  heterophylla 144
  x *hybrida* 222
  intermedia 128, 214, 216
  leucoblasta 219
  linearis 130, 193, 216
  macrantha 143, 146
  macrophylla 143
  menziesii 146, 220
  'Millbrook Road' 219
  miniata 219
  modesta 144, 146
  montana 216
  'Moora' 219
  'Muchea Pink' 219
  'Nagamoto' 222
  natalensis 134, 184, 218
  nitidula 138, 139, 219
  x *obovata* 216
  peltata 144, 145, 220
  platypoda 147
  platystigma 219
  pulchella 140, 219
  prolifera 221
  pygmaea 138, 139, 218
  ramellosa 147
  regia 136, 218
  rotundifolia *16*, *120*, 121, 122, 126–7, 193, 214, 215
  schizandra 147, 186, 214, 221
  scorpioides 219
  spathulata 133, 183, 214, 216
    'Kansai Type' 133, 183
    'Kanto Type' *132*, 133, 183
    'New Zealand Type' 133, 183
  stolonifera 146
  subhirtella 144
  sulphurea 144
  'Toodyay Pink' 219
  trinervia 218
  x *wateri* *222*
  zonaria 143
Droseraceae 99–101, 119, 155, 161
Drosophyllum lusitanicum 15, 16, 19, 95, 99–100, *101*, 208–9
Drummond, J. 96
Drummond's Sundew 140

Elliott, S. 40
Ellis, J. 155
English Sundew 128, *129*, 193, 214, 216, *217*
enzymes 13, 30, 18, 78–9, 91, 96, 100, 107, 110, 121, 167–8
epiphytes 12, 165
Erickson, R. 8, 91, 138
esterase 79, 100, 110, 121, 168

Fairy Aprons 166, 177, 227
Fan-Leaved Sundews 146–7
feeding, *see* under species name in cultivation section
'fishtail' nectary 72
Flora Caroliniana 40
flowers, *Aldrovanda* 161

Index

Byblis 98
Cephalotus 90
Darlingtonia 73, *202*
Dionaea 159
Drosera 121, *124*, 136, *138*
Drosophyllum 100
Nepenthes 79
Pinguicula 104, *105*, 112, *113*, *115*, *117*
Polypompholyx 180, *181*
Sarracenia 25, *26*, *33*, *175*, *182*
Utricularia 166, *169*, *173*, *178*, *179*
foliar feeding 20
Folkerts, R. C. 38
Fork-Leaved Sundews 148–53
fungi, carnivorous 18
fungicides 199, 204

Gemmae 111, 138, *139*
Genlisea 15, 16, 19, 92–4
Gerard's *Herbal* 46, 112, 127
glands, digestive 21, 29, 78, 91, 94, 96, 100, 107, 121, 159, 162
glands, mucilage-secreting 16, 17, 20, 94, 96, 100, 104, 107, *109*, 121, 122, 162, 167
glands, nectar-secreting 23, 29, 72, 77, 90, 91, 159
glands, retentive 96
glands, sugar-secreting 167
Great Sundew 128, *129*, 193, 214, 216, *217*
Greater Bladderwort *16–17*, *165*, 166, *167*, 168, *169*, 225
greenhouses 186–8
heating 186–7
ventilation 186–7
Green Pitcher 35–7, 200
Gray, A. 35

Heliamphora 13, 15, 19, 20, 21–4, 29, 196
flowers 23
heterodoxa 22, 24, 196
ionasi 22, 24
macdonaldiae 24
minor 22, 24, 196
neblinae 22, 24
nutans *21*, 22, 24, 196
pitcher 21, 22–3
tatei 22, 24
trap 22–3
tyleri 24
Heneage, T. 202, 203
Herbal, Gerard's 46, 112, 127
Herbal, Lyte's 119
hibernaculum 104, 111, 125
Hooded Pitcher *14*, 25, 26, 30, 55–8, *182*, 185, 193, 200
Hooker, H. D. 122
Hooker, Sir J. D. 29
Hooker's zones 29–31, 47
humidity, *see* under species name in cultivation section
Huntsman's Cup *25*, 26, 29, 46–8, 200
hybrid *Drosera* 150, 216
hybrid *Nepenthes* *14*, 74, *76*, *81*, 84, *87*, 231–5
hybrid *Sarracenia* *63ff.*, *175*, 176, 228–30
hybrid vigour 79

Insectivorous Plants 11, 28, 119
invertase 30
Irish Butterwort *102*, *105*, 110, 111, 112, 193, 211

Jones, F. M. 44

Kupper, Prof. 78

La Ballardière 89
labelling hybrids 229–30
Lamb, J. G. D. 50
leafblade, movement in, 17, 103, 107, 110, 122, *126–7*
Lefroy, B. St. G. 50
Lentibulariaceae 19, 92, 104, 165, 180
lighting, artificial 184
light requirements *see* under species name in cultivation section
Linnaeus 31, 156, 161
lipase 30, 79
Lloyd, F. E. 8, 14, 29, 78, 91, 94, 162, 167, 172
Love Nest Sundew 128, 214, 216
Lyte, H. 119

Macfarlane, J. M. 40
marl bogs 49
Marshall, W. 104
Mazrimas, J. 9, 196, 200, 204
Mellichamp, J. 28
Modest Rainbow Sundew 144, 146
Monkey Cup 79–80
Monti, G. 161
movement in leafblade 17, 103, 107, 110, 122, *126–7*
movement of tentacles 17, 103, 121, 122
mutation, genetical 152
mycorrhizal association 12
mycelium 12

Nectar 15–16, 23, 29–30, 42
nectar roll 29, *40*, 72, 73
nectary, fishtail *70*, 72, *189*
Neisler, H. M. 35
Nepenthaceae 75
Nepenthales 19
Nepenthes 15, 19, 75ff., 188, 202–6
alata 85–6
ampullaria 82–4
bicalcarata 82
x *formosa* *76*
gracillima 206
gracilis 86, 206
x *hookeriana* 84
hybrids *14*, 74, *76*, *81*, 84, *87*, 231–5
kampotiana 206
khasiana 86, 202
maxima 86
mirabilis 79–80
x *mixta* *81*
rafflesiana *79*, 82, *83*
rajah 85
ventricosa 85, *205*
x *williamsii* *14*, 74, *87*
nitrogen 13
Northern Pitcher Plant 28, 46, 48–50, 190, 192

Okefenokee Swamp 55, 59
orchid baskets 203
Osmocote 197

Painted Sundew 143, 220
Pale Butterwort 115, 212
Pale Pitcher Plant 38–40, *51*, 185, 200
Parrot Pitcher Plant *15*, 16, 25, 58–62, 183, 200
peat 194
peat bog, artificial 190, 192
peltate leaf 19, 20

perlite 195
peroxidase 100, 121
pests and diseases, *Drosera* 213
Sarracenia 199
acid phosphatase 79, 100, 110, 121, 168
photosynthesis 11, 14
phyllodia *27*, 32, 35
Pinguicula 15, 16–17, 19, 103, 104ff., 185, 190, 210–13
alpina 113, 211
bakeriana 116
caerula 115, 193, 211
caudata *106*, *108–9*, 115–16, 183, 212
grandiflora 102, 105, 110, 111, 112, 193, 211
grandiflora ssp. *rosea* 112, 193, 211
gypsicola 116–18, 212, 213
hirtiflora 114, 211, 213
lusitanica 115, 212
lutea *114*, 115, 211
mexicana *106*, 116, 183, 211, 212
moranensis 116, 212
planifolia 211
primuliflora 212
vulgaris 104, 110, 111–12, 193, 211
Pink Fan 181
Pink Petticoats 180–1, 227
Pink Sundew 133, 218
pitcher, primitive 19
pitcher structure, *Cephalotus* 90–1
Darlingtonia 72
Heliamphora 22–3
Nepenthes 75–8
Sarracenia 28–31
Plukenet, L. 161
pollination of *Sarracenia* 228–9
Polypompholyx 15, 165, 180–1, 227
multifida 181
tenella 181
Portuguese Sundew 15, 16, 19, 99–101, 208–9
pots 193
Pretty Sundew 140, 219
prey, enticement of 75–7, 91, 94, 122–5, 159, 163
propagation, *see* under species name in cultivation section
propagators 194
protease 18, 30, 79, 91, 100, 110, 121, 168
Purple Pitcher Plant *25*, 26, 29, 46–8
Purpus, J. A. 116
Pygmy Sundews 138–41, *158*

Rafinesque, C. S. 37, 49
Rainbow Plant 15, 16, 19, 95–8
Rainbow sundews 143–6
Redcoats 173, 178, 227
Red Pitcher Plant 44, 200
ribonuclease 79, 110
rosette, generative 114
vegetative 114, *118*
Round Leaved Sundew *16*, *120*, 122, 126–7, 193, 214, 215
Russell, M. C. 143

Sand 194
Sarracenia 15, 19, 21, 25ff., 188, 193, 197–200
x *ahlsii* 68
alata 38–40, *51*, 185, 200
x *areolata* 68
x *cantabridgiensis* 68
x *catesbaei* *33*, 38–40, *66*, 68, 183, 193
x *chelsonii* 68

Index

x *courtii 66,* 68, 200
drummondii 37
x 'Evendine' *176*
x excellens 68, *69*
x exornata 68
x *farnhamii* 68
flava 25, 27, 28, 29, 31–5, 183, 184, 185, 192, *199,* 200
'Maxima' *8–9,* 28, 192, 200
var. *rugelii* 200
x *formosa 65,* 68
x *gilpini* 68
x *harperi* 68
leucophylla 25, 30, *34,* 37–8, 185, 193, 200
x 'Marston Mill' *175*
minor 14, 25, 26, 30, 55–8, *182,* 185, 193, 200
x *mitchelliana 52,* 68
x *mooreana 62–3, 66,* 68
oreophila 35–7, 200
x *popei* 68, *198*
psittacina 15, 16, 25, 58–62, 183, 200
purpurea 25, 26, 29, 46–8, 200
f. *heterophylla* 50, 200
ssp. *gibbosa* 49, 200
ssp. *purpurea* 28, 48–50, 190, 192, 200
var. *riplicola* 49, 200
ssp. *venosa* 46, 50, 53, *54, 55*
x *readii* 68
x *rehderi* 68
rubra 28, 30, 40–6, 185, 193, 200
ssp. *alabamensis* 28, 44–6, 68, 200
Gulf Coast form 43, 200
ssp. *jonesii* 28, 44, 200
ssp. *typica* 40–2, 200
ssp. *wherryi* 46, 200
sledgei 40
x *swaniana 64,* 68
x *wrigleyana 66,* 68
Sarraceniaceae 21, 25, 71
Schnell, D. E. 8, 35, 55, 58, 59, 63
Schomburgk, Sir R. 22
seed boxes 194
Shining Sundew 139, 219
Sledge, E. H. 40
Small Bladderwort 174, 184, 227
Snowy Sundew 143, 220
sooty mildew *199*
Southern Pitcher Plant 46, 50–3, 183, 185, 192
sphagnum moss 195
Spoon-Leaf Sundew 133, 183, 214, 216
Steyermark, J. 24
stolons 165, 172, 173, 178
stovehouse 188
Sun Pitchers 13, 15, 19, 20, 21–4, 29
Swamp Rainbow Sundew 144
Sweet Trumpet 28, 30, 40–6, 185, 193, 200

Tate, G. H. H. 24
temperature *see* under species name in cultivation section
tendrils, *Nepenthes* 75
tentacles, *Drosera* 119, *120,* 121, 122, *123, 126–7, 129, 145*
movement of 17, 103, 121, 1[illegible] *126–7*
terrarium 185, 206
Thread-Leaf Sundew 130, 214
Tillandsias 165
Torrey, J. 35, 71
Tradescant, J. 46
trap, *Aldrovanda* 161–3
Byblis 96
Cephalotus 90–1
Darlingtonia 71–3
Dionaea 156, *157,* 159–60
Drosera 122
Drosophyllum 100
Genlisia 92–4
Heliamphora 22–3
Nepenthes 75–8
Pinguicula 107
Polypompholyx 180–1
Sarracenia 28–31
Utricularia 165, 166–7
trap types, active 14–18
ancestral 18–20
bladder 165
flypaper 15, 16–17
lobster pot 15, 16
mousetrap 15, 18
passive 14–18
pitfall 13, 15–16, 25, 31–2, 46
primitive 22–3
spring 155
steel 15, 17–18
waterbath pitfall 46–8
windowed 55–8
trigger hairs 17–18
Aldrovanda 162
Dionaea 157, 159, 160
Utricularia 167
Tropical Pitcher Plant 75ff.
Triphyophyllum 231
tubers, *Drosera* 141
Utricularia 170, 172, 178
turions 168

Utricularia 15, 18, 19, 165ff., 186, 190, 224–7
alpina 172, 226
aquatic 165, 168–70
australis 169
calycifida 226
deightonii 174, 227
dichotoma 166, 177, 184, 227
uniflora 227
dusenii 226
endresii 166, 172, 226
epiphytic 165, 172–3
gibba 225
exoleta 225
inflata 169–70, 225
intermedia 170, 225
lateriflora 174, 184, 227
longifolia 173, 226
var. *forgetiana* 173
menzeisii 173, 178, 227
minor 169, 225
neglecta 169
nelumbifolia 165
nova-zealandiae 177, 227
peltata 174, 227
praelonga 226
prehensilis 184, 226
pubescens 174, 227
purpurea 170, 225
racemosa 226
radiata 170
reniformis 173, 226
sandersonii 177, *178, 179,* 227
stellaris 170
subulata 174, 227
terrestrial 173–8
tricolor 226
violacea 227
vulgaris 16–17, 165, 166, 168, *169,* 225, 227

Venus Fly Trap 15, 17–18, 19, 154, 155ff., 184, 193, 222–3
vermiculite 203

Warmhouse 188
watering 185, 186, 187, 194 *and see* under species name in cultivation section
Waterwheel Plant 15, 17, 19, 155, 161–3, 190, 223–4
wax 29, 47, 78
West Australian Pitcher Plant 89ff.
wetting agent 48, 78
Wherry, E. T. 35, 44, 49, 53, 58
White Trumpet 25, 30, 37–8, 185, 193, 200
windows, false 56, 57, 59, *61, 70,* 72, 90, 91
winter resting buds 104, 111, 125, 168

Yellow Trumpet 28, 29, 31–5, 183, 184, 185, 192, 200
Young W. 155